Inspired by Hyde

*An anthology of writing inspired
by the area of Hyde in Winchester*

Edited by Nicky Morris

This collection copyright © Hyde900, 2010

Copyright on individual works remains with their authors.

Published in Great Britain by Hyde900.

Hyde900 is a registered charity, number 1119099.

For more information see www.hyde900.co.uk or email literature@hyde900.co.uk .

A CIP catalogue record for this book is available from the British Library.

ISBN: 9780956588104

Design by Andy Key, andy@freewheel.org.uk.

Typeset in Book Antiqua and Lucida Sans.

Printed and bound in Great Britain by Sarsen Press, www.sarsenpress.com

Cover picture: Detail from 'Sonic Snapshots: sound marks from an aural sketchbook' by Susan Wood. Based on a visual representation of sounds recorded around the Hyde area by the artist.

Frontispiece illustration: Stone capital from Hyde Abbey. Photograph by Dr John Crook.

Interior illustrations: Images by Steve Sanderson from the series '20 Hyde Doors 2010' , unless otherwise stated.

Contents

Preface

For those who may not be in the know, Hyde900 is a community project in Winchester to celebrate the 900th anniversary of the founding of Hyde Abbey.

Practically the whole of Hyde has been involved in one way or another - there have been pockets of people working on projects such as Living History, the Environment, and the Arts. There's been the Treasures of Hyde Abbey exhibition, the Pageant and the Medieval Banquet - plus a host of other activities and events.

However, my interest has been not so much in Hyde's historical past, but more in the present day Hyde and the people who live here now. One of my biggest hobbies is writing and I'm very fortunate in that I get paid for this interest, running Creative Writing classes at Peter Symonds ACE. I knew Paul Williams was keen to create a literature group as part of the Hyde900 programme and so together we started a monthly evening meeting in the Hyde Tavern. Halloween 2008 was an ideal opening, and in the candle-lit cellar (surrounded by ghosts and ghouls, courtesy of Janet the Hyde Tavern land-lady) we read our scary poems and prose. Various themes have followed - all accompanied by appropriate Janet-décor.

Aware of how small the cellar is, and wanting to reach all of Hyde, early in 2009 we launched the Hyde900 Writers' Competition. The response was wonderful and we received well over a hundred entries - poems, short stories, dramas and articles – all with a link to Hyde, however tenuous. We have tried to include as many as possible in this anthology (others we passed on to the Living History team) and here, at last, you can see the creative writing of Hyde residents (and 'outer Hyde' people, too) in print.

A sincere thank you to everyone who entered the competition. A huge thank you to Madelaine Smith and Andy Key, who have spent many hours helping to edit and typeset this book. Finally, thank you to the core group of Hyde900 people who inspired us to make this writing journey resulting in ***Inspired by Hyde***.

Nicky Morris, 10th July 2010

The Mill Stream

by Gill Johnson

Hidden histories Hyde – hush,
Years stream, meander, softly
Dark race reflects times sacred
Eddies catch sheer spirits gone,
9 centuries glide past, 9
Only, hear the swish echo
Of a monk's soulful solo.

Gill, who lives in Crawley, wrote this poem as an acrostic of Hyde900 at the beginning <u>and end</u> of each line. As a tribute to the 7 letters and numerals, each line has 7 syllables.

Searching for Scrabble
in the Cotswolds

by Elizabeth Bewick

Three days without Scrabble would be difficult to endure, both of us addicted to playing with words, so this journey – which already is a pilgrimage – becomes at a lesser level a searching. Knowing each other so well, we have no need of explanations, still less of recriminations, but three Scrabble sets and none remembered! So now we embark on a joint search of the Cotswolds in the hope of finding another: full-size, travel-pack, or special occasion pack, any kind that makes words.

Remembering the Hyde Tavern where poets, Liberals and celebrants of Hyde900 alike hold their meetings and the pile of games provided for visitors is topped by a Scrabble set, we enquire hopefully at our first stop for refreshment: tea, coffee or alcohol (which is temporarily out of the question), sandwiches, crisps and salad, but no Scrabble. A similar disappointment at the few remaining service points on our route; what an unenterprising breed of traveller must pass this way, or alternatively a hungry crowd, thirsty also for wordgames, has cleared the shelves before us. We press on – our real end in view, after all, is the game of life, which is not played with tiles.

Arrived, we check in at The Gables, where we encounter a friendly reception, but still no Scrabble. Next day we make for the Church, part of a crowd of some three hundred friends, neighbours, fellow poets and admirers, all gathering to celebrate the life of U.A. Fanthorpe, master wordsmith, user of language of deceptive simplicity and telling truths. Friends of long standing meet each other unexpectedly, others by arrangement; young poets gaze in bewilderment at the old and famous, who settle themselves with cushions and sticks on uncomfortable church pews. I watch from my wheelchair.

The programme is long, but never boring, even when listening through a defective hearing-aid. The atmosphere is charged with a special sort of electricity, shot through with blue sparks; just to be here and to be sharing in such a tremendous outpouring is unforgettable. As each reader follows the last, the tension mounts, until in a great upsurge of emotion, we all rise to our feet to pay tribute to U.A. and to show our concern for Rosie, who has been in our hearts and minds all day. Their love for each other, expressed in their poetry and in all aspects of their life together, has brought us here today, and we know, though we play Scrabble many times, it will never again have the same poignant significance.

Elizabeth Bewick, a poet, has lived in Hyde for over 40 years.

'Air' by Janet Ayers

Expectations

by Lynne Woodward

They had teased him at the allotment: no marrow that size was going to win the support of a wife, they said. He had tried to look amused, but he just thought it stupid. Why did other men make such remarks? It made him feel out of things but it was a feeling he was used to. Back home he sought refuge in the bottom of the garden, communing with his sweet peas, and cleaning brushes. Celia was out - a coffee morning with some friends, or maybe it was the book club.

In the distance he heard shouting:

'Come on you lot, run! Get moving and give it some wellie! For gawd's sake, my great grandmother could run faster than that!'

The people on the receiving end of this abuse had paid for the pleasure, and were expecting to be rewarded with the body beautiful. Stephen doubted that they would, but he couldn't help admiring their optimism.

Turning the turps bottle upside down, Stephen soaked the old teacloth, and then wiped the brushes carefully, leaving them lying on the paving slabs to dry. The smell was toxic and he rather liked it. It reminded him of the stain remover of his childhood. You couldn't be seen at school with a jam mark on your blazer, so his mother had repeatedly rubbed at his lapels, or the front of his jumpers, complaining about his clumsiness and her lack of time to sort out all the problems he created. On the way to school the smell had reminded him of his crimes; that he could be a a bit of a wicked boy after all, not just a teacher's pet.

Knees drawn up, he leaned back against the shed, sniffing the turps and listening to a chattering robin overhead. He liked this, being quiet, being on his own. He'd been described at school as a 'bookish lad' and so, after university, had followed in the family footsteps and gone into librarianship. But his father had been a rather dull civil servant, whereas Stephen saw himself as a bit of rebel, challenging youngsters to think for themselves – though, only quietly, of course.

He had managed the arts and culture section of a library for a while, and then got a job at the regional Arts Council. Very prestigious and responsible. The interviewing board had liked his commitment to performance art and concrete poetry. Now he managed quite large budgets – well, relatively speaking. A churning sensation in his stomach returned when he thought of the reports that were due, and of the organisations hoping he would bring them fame and success.

He looked at his watch and guessed that Celia would be gone for at least another hour. Freedom to dig, whistle, read the Arts pages. The robin chattered on.

When she had left this morning they had had a bristling kind of exchange. Their twenty years together had been companion-able, but she was much more ambitious than he, and he knew early on that he represented safety and security to her rather than romance. She had come to him on the rebound; a sad insecure girl, dumped by the man of her dreams and without a mother to turn to. She had turned to Stephen, and then had become dependent on him, on his comforting predictability. From the security of that base she had blossomed into running her own successful consultancy business.

At first this had been a surprise, but then he saw she had always had that kind of drive. He had found her success charm-ing, though others seemed to think he should find it a challenge to his manhood. He accepted her for what she was; on the other hand he seemed to disappoint her most of the time. When the head of department had recently announced he was taking an area of responsibility away from him and therefore decreasing his salary, Celia had been incensed, but Stephen hadn't wanted to talk about it. It wasn't that they needed the money, it was the principle of the thing, she argued. He couldn't see that it mattered so much.

Picking up his father's spade, he dug a neat hole for the box plant he'd just bought. He pressed in the earth around its roots and momentarily willed it into a huge sculpted bird. But then he saw it for what it was; a thin, straggly plant that would take many years to look like anything worth having.

He thought of the party of Americans digging a few hundred yards away in the park. He had heard there were no signs of the bones of King Alfred, and this was no surprise since they'd probably been stolen from the Abbey hundreds of years ago. But the archaeological team had deemed it appropriate to dig for the bones, so dig they did, and no doubt they all dug with high hopes.

He leaned against the shed wall, the robin still chattering overhead. Then, the chattering stopped. There was a thump; the cat from next door. Stephen reached for the garden hose, but it wasn't turned on at the tap so a dribble of water came out and the cat was not impressed. It gazed at Stephen and then slithered around the foot of the ash tree and onto a warm hump of earth near the new box plant. Cats' eyes are menacing, he thought; nothing loveable about them at all. Stephen hissed, but it didn't move. He growled. Still it didn't move. Then he got up and lunged towards it, and it scooted out of reach to the foot of the fence. He watched it pawing the ground, disturbing a small bit of earth, and leaning towards it to catch the scent. Stephen decided to ignore it.

A plane went overhead, low and thundering. He imagined the people packed inside, full of anticipation. He couldn't understand why anyone would want to do that sort of thing – pay all that money and travel all that way, only to end up frustrated and disappointed, as they inevitably would once they reached their destination. He preferred to spend time at home, pottering, no particular goal in mind. Ignoring cats, for instance.

Now the cat was mewing. Must have found a mouse, or a rat more likely –here to make a home under his decking, after a good day out in the water meadows. Hopefully it was a dead one, though he didn't want to have to deal with a rat corpse either. He lunged again at the cat with his fiercest Bengal tiger sneer, and this time the cat gave up, leaping up and over the other side of the fence.

Stephen looked at the bit of the earth where the cat had been. He couldn't see anything but he was curious what had held the cat's attention for so long. He pushed the spade lightly into the earth and raised it again, and as the spade tilted and the chalky earth fell off, something heavier fell with it to the ground. At first he thought it was an ossified dog turd, but on closer inspection it looked like something more solid than that. He picked it up with forefinger and thumb and placed it in the palm of his hand. It was some kind of metal, perhaps a bit of an old pipe. The metal was a dull grey, and ornamented with wavy lines. He thought it could be an old ring, and scraping at its centre he uncovered a central china blue coloured stone. He weighed it in his hand – it was really heavy.

He sat back against the shed with the small, cold object in his hand. Bright, sunlight struck his face and made him close his eyes. His body relaxed in the warmth. Treasure. Stephen smiled. And then he smiled again.

Of course, it could be a piece of costume jewellery, from Woolworth's, maybe from the 1960s, bought alongside the penny dip, unnoticed all these years, covered in dirt and earth, no longer looking its best, no longer shiny bright and desirable. He sat there for some time, thinking, listening to his own steady breathing. Then he slipped the ring into his pocket. Later, back in the house, he took some soft pink tissue paper from the bureau in the dining room and wrapped the ring loosely inside.

Celia came home in a flurry of bags and boxes, having returned, not from a book club meeting, as he'd thought, but from a shopping trip to Bournemouth. She plonked herself down on the sofa and pulled off her shoes.

'Be a darling and get me a coffee? I'm beat.'

Stephen went into the kitchen, started the espresso machine, and five minutes later returned with a small black china cup and an almond biscuit.

'You are a dear,' Celia intoned. 'Just how I like it.'

Stephen smiled.

'I got you something,' he said.

'For me? Where from? Have you been out?'

'Yes, for you, and I have been out, yes.'

'Oh goodie,' said Celia, 'I love presents. What is it?'

He placed the small pink package in her outstretched hand.

'Oh!' she squealed, rather overdoing it Stephen thought, 'a special gift for me!'

Stephen's face gave nothing away, so she started to unwrap the present. When she saw the dirty bit of metal lying in the paper she looked up at Stephen, waiting for some kind of explanation. But there was none.

'What is it?'

'It's a ring. I found it in the garden. Probably been there for years, unnoticed,' said Stephen.

'It's filthy,' said Celia, holding the ring at a distance in front of her, 'what would I want with that?'

'I thought you might like it. It's rather original, and beautiful in its own way. I thought you might like to have it – wear it even.'

Celia seemed not to know what to say, which was unusual. Her expression was blank, though her head was turned in his direction. It was as if he wasn't really there. Then she turned her head away.

'Well I wouldn't.'

They were now both looking down at the table, and the ring lying there, next to its discarded pink and crumpled skin. Then Celia went upstairs to the bathroom to soak in essence of oil of bergamot.

Stephen stayed downstairs cradling a mug of tea, staring at his brown leather shoes, and the familiar red-striped rug beneath them. He'd been here for years, he thought, largely unnoticed. He called a friend, and an hour later slipped through the front door with a small tartan holdall.

Before he had left the house he had planted another straggly box plant at the bottom of the garden, and at the same time dug up another seven mud-caked items. This time he didn't wrap them in pink tissue paper, but placed them in an old tea towel from the kitchen, folding the sides together carefully and then placing it in his bag. He had decided not to take much else with him. Starting again wasn't going to be difficult now - though he didn't have any particular expectations.

When taking a break from digging for treasure in her garden in Nuns Road, Lynne rings the bells at Winchester Cathedral. She is member of Hyde Writers' group, and in 2009 was one of the people who got to spend an hour on the plinth in Trafalgar Square.

Hyde Scarecrows

by Marcus Hicks

"I don't want to go to the allotment!" whined Marcus.

"Why not?" said his mum

"Because of the scarecrows. I don't like the scarecrows."

"Don't be ridiculous, you aren't scared of the scarecrows, you aren't a crow, are you? Last week you were scared of the water rats, the week before it was the swans and the week before that it was the tomatoes. You're coming with us and that's final," said mum crossly.

Just then the phone rang. It was Bill.

"Yes," shouted Marcus, saved by the bell. Bill always rescued him from going to the allotment. "Mum can I go to Bill's? I'd only moan at the allotment if I went there."

"OK, but you're coming next time"

"Not if Bill phones," whispered Marcus under his breath.

Marcus ran all the way to Bill's using the secret path from the church path onto Egbert Road. As he ran up the path he was sure he caught sight of a scarecrow's head looking out over the hedge. Can't be, thought Marcus, but he ran a bit faster just in case. When he got to Bill's, Bill was already bouncing up and down on his trampoline. Marcus joined in. After ten minutes of bouncing they decided to go to the park. They walked down Egbert Road and then Monks Road. At the black bridge Bill and Marcus stopped. Someone was in the way.

"Excuse me!" shouted Bill. The man didn't move. "Excuse me!!" shouted Bill a second time and again there was no response.

"It's a scarecrow," said Marcus "just duck under his arms and run for it". They ran into the cricket nets and looked back to see if they were being chased. "He hasn't moved" said Marcus, "I wonder what is going on, it's just like that episode in Dr Who when the scarecrows came to life."

"You know what I think?" said Bill, "Terrorists". But then Bill had thought tourist information was terrorist information.

They continued on through the park towards the playground. They headed to the swings and started to see who could go highest. Before there could be a winner Bill screamed, "Argggh" and nearly fell off the swing.

"What's the matter?" said Marcus.

"There's a scarecrow on top of the climbing frame castle".

Marcus looked up at the climbing frame and sure enough there was another scarecrow.

"Arggh," screamed Marcus and did fall off the swing.

"Let's go home," they both shouted. Marcus' house was the closest but they didn't want to go back over the black bridge and past the scarecrow again. So they went across the car park and into King Alfred Place. Their friend James lived there. "Let's tell James," said Marcus. But as they turned into James garden they saw yet another scarecrow.

"Let's not," said Bill, "Let's just run". As they got to Marcus' house his parents were just arriving and had picked up the local newspaper, on the front was a picture of a scarecrow.

"You see," said Bill, "terrorists".

"Actually," said Marcus' dad, "Hyde has been chosen by Anthony Gormley for his latest art project called *Scaring The Birds*".

"Well he certainly scared me and Bill," said Marcus.

Marcus Hicks goes to St Bede School and lives in Monks Road.

'If she hadn't gone back for her coat...'

by Madelaine Smith

It was colder than she thought,
that February morning.
Rain fell,
softly at first, then more persistent,
soaking into her cardigan.

Mother's warning, 'You'll catch your death'
echoed on.
Cold fingers of water
rolled from gas mask box,
crept into uncoated clothing.

Wet or late?
She shivered and turned,
hesitated, turned again.
Home wasn't far -
lanky legs ran all the way.

Arms sleeved in haste,
warmth wrapped round,
buttons buttoned.
Mother's warning, 'You'll be late,'
a smile and a wave goodbye.

On time, the King Alfred bus
grumbled away with wartime effort -
another would follow.
Coated in shyness,
she waited.

Unfamiliar faces -
red lipped office girls,
working men -
a different busload -
definitely late.

Clouds droned,
All eyes looked up,
No siren wailed.
Her coat was no protection
against the rain of rubble.

Madelaine Smith lives in Nuns Road. Her poem was inspired by the Hyde Street Bomb - 9 February 1943 - in which Betty Hutchings, aged 12, of 51 Nuns Road was killed on her way to catch a bus to school. Madelaine says, 'Having spoken with Betty's brother John his words "if she hadn't gone back for her coat" haunted me until the poem was written.'

The Gardens of St. Bartholomew's Church

by Richard Stillman

Pale gravestones prop up shallow flowerbeds;
the gardens flourishing better than the slate.
I can make out a single letter here, a curl there,
but that is all. From a leaf I can guess at a flower
but from this 'D' I cannot guess at a life.

A quiet corner is set aside for ashes.
I am careful how I breathe, how I pray
amongst the mild purples and soft browns
of the leaves fallen like autumn confetti,
as if joy was felt in spreading this solemn beauty.

I am enjoined to pray for those in a book
of remembrance, but it is locked away in the church,
so I pray for those forgotten, or rather lost.
I pray despite my doubts, perhaps for them,
perhaps for me. The words are enough in themselves.

The graveyard is not the place for the original:
it is undoubtedly the place of the timeless;
a working through of an obvious theme;
I am not changed by a fragment of new music,
instead I hear echoes, remember and move on.

*Richard Stillman is Head of English Literature at Peter Symonds College
and a member of the Hyde Tavern Writers group.*

Celluloid Husband

by Kath Whiting

He's gone and I am lost. There's nothing missing; I've ripped the house apart. Nothing missing, except this huge, Brian-shaped hole. Yesterday evening I thought maybe his train was delayed. He'd left his mobile on the bedside table, like he always does. Like he always did. At 10pm I called his business partner, Justin.

'Sorry Kay, he didn't come to work. I was going to call you actually, thought he must be sick.'

By midnight I'd phoned the police, they took perfunctory details, assured me he'd soon be home. And here I am today, scrabbling through his stuff. Brian's not like this; he's a clock-work man, I used to tease him about it. This is how he works:

>Monday: Screen Cinema (for the cheap tickets)
>Tuesday: Footie practice at River Park
>Wednesday: Hyde Tavern with Justin
>Thursday: Tescos and Housework
>Friday: Curry and Jonathan Ross
>Saturday: Walk to St Catherine's Hill and out for a Meal
>Sunday: Play Footie

He missed our Tescos and Housework night.

The phone goes and I leap out of my chair. 'Brian?'

'Sorry Kay, it's Justin.'

'Oh.'

'He didn't come home then?'

'No,' I say, 'Justin?'

'Yes?'

'Did he…is he…do you know if he…?'

'Kay, there isn't anyone else. I'd know. Or you'd know. He's just not like that.' He is silent for a moment and then continues, 'Have you…have you called around the hospitals?'

I let out a huge sob, I can't help it. I hadn't thought of that.

'Look,' he says, 'I'll do that. You call Missing Persons.'

Missing Persons are now 'Missing People'. I suppose that makes sense, grammatically. They are kind, warm and entirely professional. They ask for a photo, so I dig out our old albums from the loft. And there's his face, in front of me: Brian dressed as a pirate, Brian pulling a silly face, Brian eating an Ice cream. But they're all frozen and anyone that knows/knew him knows he was never still. I realise what I need is tape, I need to see him moving. I dust off the old video player and carry it downstairs, a box of cassettes balanced on top of it. After a while I locate one of him playing the drums as a teenager.

I call, email and text everyone I can think of, for footage of him. I say it's for a birthday surprise. I don't say he's gone. Then I sit back on the doorstep and wait for my disappeared man.

After four hours I creak off the step and call the police again. This time they ask lots of questions. Are we happy? Is he having an affair? Am I having an affair? Do we argue? Do we use drugs? How would I describe our home life? I end up feeling like *I'm* being accused. I put the phone down.

It's Jonathan Ross night and here I am crying into my prawn biriani.

After a night of nightmares, I continue my doorstep vigil. The concrete of the step is cracked and a dandelion is growing out of it. Tiny red mites scuttle, busily going about their lives, not like me, I'm not going about anything. I'm staring down at my new companions when I hear steps.

I see him through my tears, 'Brian!'

But of course it's not Brian; it's the postman. He has several brown parcels and some envelopes.

'You alright, love?'

'Just waiting for…for the post.' I give him a watery smile.

'Birthday?'

I shake my head and take the parcels from him.

'Well, take care of yourself.' He pats me on the shoulder and carries on his round.

I wait until he's gone and then tear open the packages, right there on the doorstep. There are three videos, four DVDs and his uncle has even sent a canister of cine-film. I collect it all together, go indoors and check my email. The download takes a while but I am rewarded with six media clips.

So I won't forget Brian while I wait, I will watch him. I watch him over and over, at all these celebrations; at weddings, at parties, playing football. And he looks so happy. He's just there in the computer, on the TV. If only I could climb in and join him or get him out. My days are now divided into doorstep waiting and watching all this. But more and more I just watch Brian on the screens. And then, after a week of watching, I feel him. I feel him next to me, just out of eye shot, no longer made of flesh, made of videotape and celluloid and thousands and thousands of noughts and ones.

'You've come back.'

'I'm always with you,' this shadow Brian says and leans into my shoulder to watch another video with me. The telephone rings and he dissipates.

'Kay, it's Justin.'

'Hi Justin.'

'Any news?' his voice sounds tired.

'News? I haven't watched the news.' Brian's not a child; the news only reports missing children.

'Do you want me to come round, Kay?'

'No no, that's okay. No thank you. Bye.'

I know if I can focus hard enough I can bring him back to me.

No more numb bum on the doorstep. I lug the second television down from the bedroom so I can play videos on it and I play DVDs on our main one. I pull all the photos out of our albums and put the media clips on continuous play on my laptop. I even find an old projector on eBay.

The postman delivers it the following week. I'm no longer teary and still in my dressing gown. Today I'm cheery and wearing my blue dress, my husband's favourite.

'You're a popular lady,' the postman wheezes with the large package.

'Yes.'

'Do you want a hand in with it?' he asks.

'Oh no, I'll manage,' I say, taking it off him.

Ten minutes later, when it's all running and whirring and buzzing and there is Brian on three screens and projected on the wall, he appears again. Now I can see him properly; I've found him.

This Brian is easier going than the real one. He doesn't care what's for dinner, doesn't want tea and coffee, doesn't mind if I break 'the routine'. He is the essence of good Brian. He even replies now when I talk to him. Smiles gently at me when I turn the light out at night. He's made of the happy bits from all the happy video of him.

On 'Hyde Tavern with Justin' day a policewoman comes round. I'm better at focusing now and Brian doesn't vanish. He winks at me and makes funny faces while the constable asks questions. I have to try and contain my giggles. She looks around at all the photos I've papered the walls with.

'Is there anyone who can look after you?'

The video player hisses to a stop. 'Oh excuse me a moment,' I rewind the tape and start it again. 'That's better. What were you saying?'

'Anyone who can stay with you for a little while?'

'Oh no, I'm okay thank you.'

She doesn't ask many more questions, just takes Justin's phone number. When I show her out I hear the cine-film flappering to an end. I rush back to start it again.

On the Friday we are sitting with a Chinese and watch a romantic comedy, when the phone goes. It's Justin.

'Kay, we've found Brian.'

I look at my celluloid husband. He smiles at me, shrugs and disappears.

Kath Whiting lives in Upper Brook Street. She contributes to the Hyde900 'Bring-Your-Own-Literature' events in the Hyde Tavern Cellar.

Moving on

by Neil Hyman

Between our houses, in that red
ravine between our houses, I
am ambushed by the dispossessed.
They left. They went to relatives;
they went to other houses or
to hospital ... They'd always said
they wanted fewer or more stairs,
some place where they could work or rest,
that Salter's mutton didn't suit ...
and no doubt, some of them, to war.

Not yet though. No, not yet. Instead
they take a knife, these people, from
the kitchen drawer – take it round
the side and carve initials, names,
dates into the brick. *A G
1913, D PALMER, FRED.*
They carve, Dad whistles, Ma lines up
a seam. Yet war is now as bound
to come as is the river always
to slip past here to the sea.

So if they thought they'd never tread
somewhere not England they were wrong,
and come back, though so not the same
A G '13 will seem as if

it should be on the Menin Gate.
They'll wheel the bike through to the shed
and glance at what they've added since.
A G 1919 will frame
and mark an end to it ... The next
year they plant bulbs and decorate.

Neil Hyman, from Monks Road, thanks Hyde900 for reviving an old interest in writing poetry.

A Wall Story

by Neil Dewey

Desmond Hickett leaned his elderly forehead against the hot stone block.

'Today: is it today?'

His lips didn't move. Nor his vocal chords.

'How much longer?' The breath he had held, waiting yet again for a reply, expired in a weary sigh.

The old wall, its mixture of ancient dressed and undressed stone, capped with more recent bricks, all of which had been re-pointed so many times during the last millennium, remained silent.

Desmond turned away, through 180 degrees. He stepped off the railway sleeper platform he had placed behind a mature and almost blowsy *Fatsia Japonica* to screen his barbecue area from the upper storey eyes of his neighbours. Different grades of gravel scrunched a brief backing track to the constant tone of the sub-station next door as he took his eight measured paces to the open patio door. He slid it to behind him, sealing out the noise. As usual, the silence inside was oppressive, somehow emphasising his long wait. After making a beaker of green tea he opened the door a crack. The diminished drone that snuck in was a comforter of sorts.

'Today?'

The sun was higher now. In theory, he thought, its highest point was at noon. Or was it one... or eleven with the clock changes? Celestial and temporal differences constantly defeated him. He could smell the heat of the wall from the edge of the sleepers, an old sturdy contentment that mingled with the newer flashy aromatics of the coal tar that preserved the wood. Desmond moved forward and ran his hands over the familiar blocks, welcoming himself back, re-establishing contact with

27

the hard smooth flints, the fine gritty surface of the crudely dressed stones, the soft, dustier, homely feel of the rubble.

'Today: is it today?'

His head buzzed with the blaring lunchtime sun that threatened to more than bronze his pate. The sub-station's tenor hum was a counterpoint that swelled in his consciousness to an internal vibration that masked all awareness of his body save the warmth that played through his hands and the hard contact of his forehead.

'I can't do this much longer,' he thought. 'My wife. She's found a buyer for the house. They'll not know about... They won't speak to you properly.' He paused, then began to slowly butt his head against the stone his forehead had rested on. Years of frustration had left a light but discernible grease mark on the wall and a callous at the hairline long lost. 'You could tell me so much. I'm always ready to listen. Please?'

The low frequency throb inside him was replaced by an appreciation of his self-inflicted pain. He ceased his head banging, but as he resumed his one-sided conversation, head on wall, the hum returned to his ears, stepped up to a drone, then to an intense manic buzz that filled his mind – a screaming, sawing noise that briefly reminded him of the day as a child when a small insect flew inside his left ear with such startling sonic effect that he careered around the garden, gouging the ear with his little finger until blood streamed down his neck, and the angry sound subsided stickily in the waxy depths.

This time, he didn't think to beat at his ears, to move his hands from the wall, let alone cut himself off from the noise's source. The fleeting childhood comparison vanished as the buzz intensified to a high-pitched whine that whipped every nerve ending to a state that should have made him cry out, had not the crackle and shock of high voltage glued his hands and head to the wall and caused him to swallow his tongue.

The excruciating electric prickle and dental-drill like screech that only he could hear swelled to a mind-bending crescendo, and then both collapsed, the noise turning back on itself in a short sharp plughole-like swallow – a reality that aped the imaginings of Science Fiction sound effects.

Soon, somehow – out of the absolute silence –

'Oh go on then,' the wall indicated… implied… insinuated… inferred… intimated.

There was no word for it in what was left of Desmond's brain.

'Oh, go on then – might as well. You've asked often enough. Such admirable persistence deserves a reward, I suppose. Although I have to admit, I'm getting a little sick of your pleading.'

'So is it today? The Solstice? Was it…?'

'Is that all you can think to say – in the circumstances.' It sighed. 'Good Lord, no, nothing to do with that.'

The wall shimmied with amusement, or so it seemed to Desmond.

'Well… obviously, yes, it is today… when you finally get to hear from me. To listen to my stories. But don't go thinking there's anything special about Solstices and all that mumbo-jumbo, white witch, New-Earth stuff. Look – to be honest I've been a bit bored. The wet summer hasn't helped. There's nothing like a bit of sun, is there? You know, to gee one up a tad. Oh, and before you put the rain down to our local Saint what's-his-name… Swithin, Swithun… d'you know, there's even a source that claims a Swith-hun. Heavens, you lot can't even agree his spelling. Anyway, it's nothing to do with him – it's pure science – the theory about the Jet-Stream holds more water.'

The wall wobbled at some more of its mirth. 'Water? St Swithin? Stream?' The wall huffed in frustration at Desmond's lack of humour. 'OK, not a classic joke, sorry, but I'm feeling a little frisky today, and right now you're probably not at your best. Now then, where was I? I know – our venerable Saint. Well, I could tell you a few stories.' He tutted, 'What *am* I saying… Now you are here, sort of with me, I *have* to tell you all of them – and you can forget broken eggs and bridges and malicious workmen, and most of the other tales too. Not, mind

29

you, that they're untrue. No, they're just hopelessly inaccurate, laced with all sorts of religious codswallop aimed at pumping up his reputation and justifying his Sainthood. Poor old boy was awfully embarrassed about that, you know. Not his sort of thing at all. And he's far from happy about his old bones being split up and spread all over the place.

'Still, here I am, rambling on, loosening up the metaphysical tonsils before I get down to the real deal. You want the truth, what I've witnessed. In the right order. No gossip. Fine. It'll take some time, though. Quite a long while actually. But it's such a relief, I can tell you, to have someone interested, the right amount of power readily available and, and what do you call it? Ah yes, wireless internet.

As the wall spoke, the laptop in Desmond's study lit up and text scrolled rapidly down a screen headed *Word 2007 – Silchester Place Wall Tells All*. Outside, in the courtyard garden, three charred marks on the old wall and a modest pile of greasy ash were to be the only reminder of Desmond.

Neil Dewey hopes to move to Hyde when he sells his house; in the meantime he enjoys the Hyde Tavern.

Where We Belong

by Abby Croucher

Just months within us meeting
It was clear that I had found
The man who made me feel complete,
Who'd turned my life around,
The man I wanted by my side
Each minute of each day,
But living thirty miles apart
Was just too far away.
With petrol on the increase
(And a speeding ticket too!),
We had to find a home to share
And anywhere would do.

With my work in Southampton
And with him based up in Woking,
He used his transport planner's head
(you might think that I'm joking!)
And came up with the idea that
By living near a station,
On trains from different platforms
We'd both reach our destination.
So Winchester was talked of
As the place where we'd reside,
And sure enough we came across
The perfect place in Hyde.

The stream, the ducks, the gate, the pub,
It looked so very pretty,
Ten minutes from the station
And ten minutes from the city.
And then we saw the quaint, old church,
And straight away we knew,
That this was going to be where we
Would stand and say 'I do'.
We'd found the place we felt we'd live
A long and happy life –
What better way to start it than
Becoming man and wife?

So soon he popped the question,
Preparations were begun,
We booked the time and venue,
Found the dress which was 'the one'.
The bridesmaids all were chosen,
And the page boy and best man,
The wedding cake was ordered
And the honeymoon all planned,
The wedding rings were crafted,
We decided on the flowers,
(The King Alf's hanging baskets
Wouldn't be as nice as ours!).

But one thing worried others –
That we hadn't booked a car
To take us to Bartholomew's
(although it wasn't far).

I hoped, the date approaching,
That the weather would remember
To keep the rain away
On Friday 18th September,
To let me, in my wedding dress,
Walk through the streets of Hyde
To meet the man I loved so much,
The proudest ever bride.

Abby Croucher moved to Hyde in 2008 and married Matt Croucher the following year at St Bartholomew's.

A Midsummer Swing

by Karen Marsh

The swing swung rhythmically, catching slightly on the return. Four feet brushed petals on the daisies, two hands gripped, merging sixty-five years of togetherness. This was all they had left.

'I know love,' whispered Eva, reading the watery pools of Wilf's eyes.

She watched as one side of his mouth tried to form a word against the bubbles of saliva, and gently stroked the frozen side of his face with the back of her fingers in reward for his effort.

'You save your energy now, let me do the talking – you always said I could carry a conversation on my own. And a lot's happened in the garden since...well, you know,' Eva sniffed, and caught her sob in the back of her throat, contorting her lips to contain it.

They had moved to this house, in Nuns Road, as newlyweds. While Wilf worked six days a week at the factory, Eva created the home and garden they held in a shared vision. They were a living and breathing 1950's cliché.

The house had matured with them, adapting with the stages of life, stalling on some. The nursery that had been filled with expectation for eight months lay enshrined in a psychedelic time warp. Wilf and Eva returning home from the hospital, empty armed and broken hearted, had permanently locked the door on their family.

Even after Wilf retired they kept to the familiar routine, up with the larks ready for a breakfast spent planning the day. The chirruping dawns of June signalled the start of dining on the patio. Against the deafening crunch of toast under the knife edge, they would sit for half the morning observing the wildlife. Their resident robin would hop onto the edge of the table, now experienced in securing the crumbs of the crust which were too hard for ill fitting plastic teeth. Even the magpies were welcomed with a salute and a bobbing of heads in well practised superstition.

The browning flower heads of Lily of the Valley made way for the blood red poppies exploding across the borders almost in a blink against the solstice sun.

Wilf and Eva were the hardy annuals, conducting the well rehearsed floral concert with perfection from their wooden bench.

In the evenings they moved to the swinging chair, a retirement gift for years of faithful service. Lovingly maintained with 3-in-1, Hammerite, and a new set of covers made by Eva, it weathered the to and fro stoically over the next twenty years.

The reassuring creek of the springs announced the swaying to the fledglings floating out of the nesting box on the lilac tree for the first time. Gentle trickling water from the weathered maiden's vase, and the cooing of the doves from the roof built to a subtle crescendo of nature on the first day of summer this year. The season began so promisingly.

The finale was close the next morning when Eva, intent on buttering her toast heard the cymbals crash, as the stainless steel dropped from Wilf's grip chipping into the paving slab on landing. The wooden chair creaked as its inhabitant slumped to one side, knocking the cup and sending a river of tea across the slatted wood, drip dripping through the gaps.

Eva froze, her knife still raised, butter hanging expectantly from its serrated edge.

The discarded breakfast things lay strewn on the patio for the next few days. Eva held her position by the hospital bed, until the doctors broke the news.

'It's all right love, I'm taking you home,' Eva reassured Wilf.

The swing was their observation point for the last sun at dusk. It was Eva's observation point for the dusk of Wilf's life.

Her hand was still hanging on to him as she rested her cheek against his and lightly danced her eyelashes on his skin. They had giggled as teenagers on first discovering the innocent pleasure this could bring, and the teenager was still alive in Wilf's eyes as he turned for one last look at Eva.

They had each other, that was all they needed.

They had had each other, now Eva was alone.

It was a week before Eva could face venturing into the garden again. She dropped onto the swing, feeling unsteady as it swung away with her. Two feet brushed the ground, one hand gripped the swing and the other covered the sigh from her mouth, as she took in the sight in front of her.

As the chaffinches branched out from the nesting box heralded by the pink, pink of their call, the borders came to life with irises and carnations swaying, hydrangeas flowing and violets popping up in between. The heady scent of old fashioned roses swirled in the breeze, as the resident robin hopped onto the arm of the swing. Eva smiled.

'All right girl?' Wilf would have said to her

'I am now,' she whispered.

Karen Marsh lives in Winchester and comes to the Hyde900 'Bring-Your-Own-Literature' events at the Hyde Tavern.

The Statue Wakes Up!

by Edward Agombar

People were throwing confetti at King Alfred's Statue because it was the anniversary of his birth. It brushed against the stone and when everyone went home he woke up. It was a dark and spooky night and owls were twittering. King Alfred jumped off the stone plinth and caught a bus to Hyde to find his remains. He had heard people talking about the three graves in Hyde and he wanted to find them.

He started walking around. First he walked down Saxon Road but he couldn't find any Saxons! Then he went to Egbert Road but he couldn't find King Egbert's Castle! He went on to Arthur Road but he couldn't find King Arthur. He thought to himself, "Everything has changed!" Suddenly he saw his name – King Alfred Place so he started to walk towards it. He found the three graves at the bottom of the road. He got his sword out and cut around the middle one. He couldn't find anything, so he yawned and climbed up a tree and thought, "I'll dig it out tomorrow".

In the night King Alfred rolled out of the tree and into the hole. He smashed the ground with his great big sword and woke up with a hot burning smell of magma and rock. He found himself in the centre of the earth. He started to move towards the crust of the earth with the magma and rock. He thought the world was getting narrower. When he got to the top he was in a different country. King Alfred found himself in a volcano. Lava was pouring down the side of the volcano. Suddenly there was a big bang! He flew through the air and landed on the stone plinth back where he started.

Back in Hyde, something was happening underneath one of the gravestones. Because King Alfred's statue had dug one of the stones up, he had woken the bones of King Alfred's body.

The bones began to dig himself out. When they had got out they started to look for King Alfred's statue.

It was Halloween. Some people went out trick and treating. When people saw the skeleton they thought, "That's a good trick skeleton", but the skeleton just ignored them and kept walking on. By the time that he got to the statue, it was dark and the moon came out. When the skeleton saw King Alfred's Statue, the Statue jumped off the stone plinth and hugged the skeleton without breaking any bones. They walked away from the plinth and went to live together somewhere else.

People always wondered how the Statue had gone because the person who stole it would have to be very strong.

Edward Agombar, aged 7, is in Dickens Class at St Bede School.

The Kids of Egbert Road

by Caroline Owen Wintersgill

Part 1: The Horrible Horde

Way, way back, in the days when your grandma was as young and naughty as you, and a child could buy a bag of sweets as big as their head for a penny, there lived in this part of Winchester, a fierce gang of crooks. Everyone called them the Horrible Horde of Hyde.

Their leader was hideous Harold, a hook-nosed hunchback with halitosis. His partner in both life and crime was Diabolical Deirdre. She owned a pack of demented Dobermans who disrupted the nights of scores of neighbours with their late-night howling and growling. Harold and Deirdre were ugly, stupid and unpleasant, but they had nothing on Bolthead Barry, who had big boils all over his bottom. Worst of all was Lobotomy Lil: 109 years old, with lilac locks and leering lips.

Nobody was safe from the Horrible Horde. Each night they prowled the streets of Hyde, looking for loot. If your Dad laid out his suit before he went to bed, his best trousers would be on Bolt-head Barry's boily bottom before breakfast. If your Mum made a steak and kidney pie, Diabolical Deirdre would feed it to her demented dogs. Lobotomy Lil specialised in school bags. She would rummage around for completed homework and library books and set fire to them in the street just for fun. Hideous Harold was the most horrible of them all. He stole toys. In those days, children didn't have as many toys as they do now and they were very precious indeed. Harold would sneak around corners, seeking a proud child with a shiny train or a new pirate costume and as soon as their back was turned, he would swipe it. He prowled just out of sight at parties, poking the presents and pinching them before they were even unwrapped. Once he cast a fishing line through a window in

Nun's Road, hooked a teddy bear from a little boy's bed, and reeled it in to his bag of swag.

At the end of each night's evil-doings, the gang retreated to their secret bunker deep below the Gordon Road laundry. Here they would swig mouthfuls of a horrible drink called Irn Bru (which is honestly made from iron girders – if you don't believe me ask your Dad) and eat baked beans straight from the tin using a dirty penknife as a spoon. And they would show off their cache, prancing about in the clothes Bolthead Barry had purloined, playing raucously with the toys and giggling wickedly.

But, I'm sure you want to know – what did the Horrible Horde do with all these precious possessions? Did they need them to feed and clothe their own families? They did not! Did they steal from the rich to give to the poor? They did not! Did they sell everything at the car boot sale and invest the money in diamond mines, or a space mission or the international revolutionary movement? They did not! They did it *just for badness*. No other reason. So when they'd had their night of fun with the stolen swag they threw it into a disused well, deep underneath the streets of Hyde. And there it sat, for more than half a century.

Part 2: The Kids

The Kids of Egbert Road sat in their Official Headquarters: the cavernous garden shed of number 41. It was the evening before the Egbert Road Street party and they were happily exhausted after a day of war with their big rivals, The Kids of Arthur Road. The Arthur Road mob had slaughtered them at tree climbing, but the Egbert kids had triumphed in their ability to throw eggs over houses without breaking them. They were discussing their outfits for the fancy dress parade. Finn and Louis had both decided to be Spiderman so they could crawl the length of the street along the walls, without touching the ground; Ruby, Miranda, Rosanna and Nell were to be cartwheeling, pom-pom wielding cheerleaders, and one year old Florence was planning to come as Queen Boudicea, thus condemning her parents to a demanding evening of chariot-construction.

Suddenly, everyone went quiet. A mysterious sound could be heard outside the back door of the Kids' HQ: *thud, fluffl, thud, fluffl, thud, fluffl...* The noise stopped, and there was a single knock at the door. Everyone inside held their breath. Then three fast taps followed by two longer ones. The secret signal! It was a friend! In stumbled Emily, dragging an enormous trunk: 'I found this in the loft,' she said. 'It isn't my Dad's. He said it was here when he bought the house. I thought it might have some dressing up clothes in it we could use for tomorrow.'

Everyone crowded round as the trunk creaked open. Inside was an enormous pair of suit trousers with braces, six pairs of holey, greying underpants, a shapeless dress in violent shades of lilac and mouldy green, and a moth-eaten brown shawl. The kids were very disappointed. 'I wouldn't wear these things if they were the last clothes on earth in a freak snowstorm,' said Edward.

But as they pulled the shawl from the trunk, something clattered to the floor: it was a bone!

'Part of a skeleton,' shouted Milo, 'it's a real life murder mystery! And if the kids of Egbert Road solve it we'll be famous. We'll get in the Hampshire Chronicle and get a medal from the police'.

Emily came over and took a closer look. 'I hate to disappoint you Milo, old sausage, but I don't think this bone is human. Check out the bite marks - this is the kind of bone the butcher gives me for our dogs.'

With reluctance Milo had to admit she was right, the bone had been well-chewed and there were also horrible bits of decomposing dog-biscuit amongst the trunk's contents.

'My sister Georgina did a project on the history of our house,' continued Emily. 'It was once owned by an old couple called Harold and Deirdre Drivelweed. They were completely bonkers by all accounts. They had something like fourteen dogs and they ended up in jail after the police caught them stealing the carpet in the King Alfred pub'.

'Jail, for a bit of carpet!' exclaimed Noah.

'Actually', said Eve, 'it wasn't just the carpet. The wise women of Egbert Road had been onto that pair for months. They were part of some local gang apparently. Haven't you ever heard the older people round here talk about them? They were mean as anything. Stole toys and never gave them back. Mrs Abbot told me her favourite doll disappeared one night and she still misses her all these years later.'

As Emily and Eve were telling the history of the Horrible Horde, some of the smaller children - bored by the endless talking - had jumped into the trunk.Tom, William and Grace were throwing dog biscuits at each other; Jack, Joshua,Tom, Benji, Arthur and Thomas had put Harold's old underpants on their heads for a joke; and Isabel, Jonathan, Astrid and Joe had found a box of chalks and were tearing and scribbling on strips of the yellowing paper that lined the trunk.

Suddenly, out of the corner of his eye, Louis spotted something – a pattern chalked onto the lid of the trunk behind the lining paper. He beckoned Finn and they took a closer look: a wiggly blue line at the top, below it a cross-hatching of white lines, at the centre a scribbled figure with a yellow hat waving a stick, and on the right a house with an enormous chimney. Between the two drawings stretched a thick brown line.

'What on earth is that?' breathed Louis.

'Well, it certainly isn't art,' laughed Finn. 'I'd say it's a map, a bit of a rubbish one but I think I can work it out. That blue line is the river, and the white lines below it are the streets – look, that must be Nun's Road, then Saxon Road. Dunno about the geezer with the hat though'.

By this time the story was finished, and the kids turned to hear what all the fuss was about.

'Wow! A treasure map!' exclaimed Jonah.

'Hmmm', said Finn, 'could be, but there's no spot marked X. How do we know where the treasure is?' They all studied the drawing, but nobody could make any more sense of it. What could it all mean? Suddenly little Florence jumped up and down.

'Wuhwuh eggy,' she said – and grabbing a blue chalk, she scribbled all over her big toenail.

'Er, does anybody speak Florence?' asked William.

The kids looked blank, but Rosanna piped up, 'Clever girl! She says we must ask the Wise Women of Egbert Road!'

Part 3: The Wise Women

Egbert Road may look very ordinary, but far beneath the streets and houses, there is ancient magic at work. More than a thousand years ago, this was the domain of King Egbert of Wessex, grandfather of King Alfred the Great. Egbert's wife, Redburga (that was honestly her name, I'm not making it up, ask your teacher if you don't believe me) was the first Wise Woman of Winchester. By modern standards she looked a bit odd. She wore a helmet on her head and she painted her feet blue with woad. But she was as wise as anything. She could read the signs of the land and sky, she could predict the future and she could make inanimate objects come to life. Ever since that time, a handful of women living in Egbert Road have been granted unusual powers. They don't have to have been born there, these powers come to them unexpectedly following a full moon. You can generally recognise a wise woman by the traces of blue on her big toenail but if you're not sure, just try saying 'Redburga' to her. If she is a true wise woman she will immediately give you a wise piece of advice.

As soon as Florence had made her suggestion, the kids of Egbert Road raced out of the shed and into the street. They had to whisper 'Redburga' to three or four surprised-looking ladies before they found the wise woman they were looking for. The kids showed her the drawing they had found in Emily's trunk.The wise woman's eyes misted over and she appeared to be talking in her sleep.

'Ah Alfred, my grandson,' she cooed. 'Ask the rabbit and you will find what you seek. The road runs straight but deep, to the black hole where the past is hid.'

'Completely mental,' sighed Tom, 'Oh well, back to the drawing board.'

'No, don't you see?' said Ruby excitedly, 'she thinks she's the original Redburga. King Alfred was Redburga's grandson. The man with the yellow hat on our map, he's actually King Alfred wearing a crown and waving his sword. I think she's telling us to go to the King Alfred pub'.

The kids raced down Danes Road, and one by one, scaled the fence into the pub garden. None of them noticed the kid from Arthur Road, the one who had beaten them all at tree-climbing earlier in the afternoon, sitting high in the branches of a tree, watching their every move. What next?

'Wedda bunna rabba?' said Florence.

Ah yes, the wise woman had said something about asking a rabbit for help. But there hadn't been a real rabbit in the pub garden for years. A toy rabbit maybe? Someone dressed up as a rabbit? The kids looked around, a trifle foolishly. Only Arthur moved confidently towards the steps that led to the back door of the pub, guarded at the top by a little stone rabbit. As the kids crowded round, he gave the rabbit's nose a little tap and whispered in his ear, 'We're looking for a road, straight and deep'. And suddenly, the little stone rabbit began to twitch, and fur started to sprout on his back. Within seconds the rabbit had jumped into the flower bed and eaten up a display of pansies, revealing a brass ring hidden underneath. The children heaved on the brass ring and discovered a trap door, with a long flight of steps running deep into the ground.

'OK, who's first?' said Nicholas.

None of them noticed the huddle of grown-ups approaching them.

'Time for bed now, children!' boomed a chorus of Mums and Dads, spoiling the fun, as they usually do.

Part 4: The Old Hyde Laundry

At 7 o'clock on the morning of the Egbert Road Street party a curious procession was seen advancing on the garden of the King Alfred pub in Hyde. Most were still in their pyjamas, though some had remembered to tuck them into welly boots, others were in cheerleading outfits, two of them were in Spider-man costumes and one very small one seemed to be dressed as Queen Boudicea and was being pushed along in a chariot by two older children. Some carried torches and spades, one had a backpack full of skipping ropes, others were simply clutching the remains of their breakfast - bowls of Cocoa Pops, bacon sandwiches, and even a half-eaten fried egg. One moment, they were all crowding into the pub garden and the next: well, if like I did that morning, you popped into the pub to get a coffee, the next moment you would have found they had all vanished into thin air, fried eggs and all.

Thirty three steps led from the pub garden to the deep, straight and very muddy underground passage the kids had found on the mysterious map. If the steps had been hard-going, especially for Emily and Noah, who were carrying Florence in her chariot, the muddy passage was even worse. It was narrow and very low overhead and in places the roof had tumbled in almost blocking their path. It seemed that no one had set foot there for half a century.

Except... except that there were four pairs of footprints still clearly imprinted on the mud. Surely they hadn't been there for more than fifty years? As the children looked anxiously at the footprints they heard something at the end of the tunnel. It was a very faint sound but it sounded a little like... could it be... the barking of a dog?

'Emily,' said Miranda slowly. 'Didn't you say that Deirdre Drivelweed had a pack of fierce dogs?'

'Yes,' said Emily, but that was more than fifty years ago, and the oldest ever Doberman only made it to twenty two.

'Yikes! A ghost dog!' yelped William, in a passable imitation of Shaggy from Scooby Doo.

Everybody giggled, but perhaps slightly nervously.

'Where d'you think we are we now?' asked Grace.

'I've been counting our footsteps', said Joe. 'I'd say we're right under St Bede's School playground.'

'Cool' said Jack. 'We've found the teachers' secret passage to the pub!'

But the path suddenly turned sharply to the right, opening into a cavern almost as big as the school hall, and completely lined with baked bean cans and empty Irn Bru bottles

'*Horra Hodda Hiddee Hidee*!' said Florence suddenly.

'Hmmm,' said Edward, 'I'm beginning to get the hang of this language. I think she means it's the Horrible Horde's Hideous Hideout. And I know where it is too. It's right underneath the Gordon Road laundry. That must be the building with the chimney on the mysterious map'.

As he spoke, the children had begun to have the uneasy feeling that they were not alone. They looked down. The footprints they had noticed earlier seemed even clearer on the muddy floor of the cave and beside them was a set of paw prints.

'What do we do now?' asked Joshua.

Nell took the lead. 'I know. I've seen it on Scooby Doo. We split up. Nicholas, Jack, Eve, Noah, Jonah, Ruby, Grace, Astrid, Joe, Tom and Benji – you're in my gang and we follow the footprints. Finn, Louis, Emily, Florence, Miranda, Arthur, Isabel, Jonathan, Edward, William and Thomas, you stay with Milo and check out the cave. There must be some reason the map led us here. Jack, William, Joshua and Baby Ben, you're on look-out, and Rosanna and Amy, you need to gather the forensic evidence.'

As Milo handed out spades and Rosanna and Amy unpacked their magnifying glasses and talcum powder, the footprint team sped off to the corner of the cave where a precarious flight of steps had been cut into the rock. The resourceful Nell pulled a long skipping rope out of her backpack and tied her team securely together before attempting the ascent. As they reached the top, they saw a trap door above their heads. Nell gave it a tentative shove and the half rotten wood split open, allowing the crew to clamber through. As they did so they were half blinded by an intense shaft of sunlight from a glass roof in the corner of the main laundry building. Blinking in the unaccustomed glare, Nell thought she saw a dark figure rounding the corner. It looked like an old lady – tiny, with lilac-white hair, in a long dress with a knitted shawl. With a shudder, she remembered Emily's description of the Horrible Horde – Harold, Deirdre, Barry and Lil. Lilac-locked Lil, who had celebrated her 109th birthday fifty years earlier.

'Um. It may have been a trick of the light, but did anyone see what I just saw?'

'I think so,' shivered Ruby, pointing to the opposite wall, 'you mean that dog that ran out of the door as we came in? It was a Doberman, wasn't it?

Meanwhile, Milo's team had picked their way through about 250 Irn Bru bottles and a mountain of baked bean cans, and using their spades to remove piles of earth and leaves, had uncovered a circle of slatted wood in the floor of the cave. Edward picked up a stone and dropped it through one of the cracks. He waited, and waited a bit longer. Several seconds later there was a faint splash.

'A well', he said, 'very deep, but hardly any water. Let's get that cover off!'

Three of the boys heaved the cover aside and the whole gang peered into the inky blackness. There was no sign of a ladder, or even a bucket they could lower down into the well.

'It's too dangerous' said Emily. 'And we don't even know that there's anything down there.'

'The wise woman did mention a black hole,' Joe reminded her. 'It's just a pity she didn't give us any clues about how to climb into it.'

Suddenly Florence started to wave her arms about excitedly. 'Pidermens!' she shouted, 'in dair suits!'

'By George, she's got it!' shouted Finn. 'What's the point of having a top of the range Spiderman suit if it doesn't stick to walls? Louis and I have been practising in these for weeks. We can get round our entire house without touching the floor once. Of course we can climb into a poxy old well'.

'Mum even made us bring the safety harnesses' said Louis ('though I really don't recommend you should try this at home,' he added, climbing into the well

Meanwhile, Rosanna and Amy were looking for clues. Rosanna was examining the doggy pawprints, trying to work out what breed it might be, but Amy was more interested in studying the human footprints. After a careful look, she whispered something to her sister. 'Just like my ones!' she concluded happily.

Rosanna was impressed. 'I think that could be an important clue, Amy,' she said

Their investigations were interrupted by a cry from the bottom of the well. 'Spidermen to base camp,' came the message, 'we've found the loot! And you've never seen anything like it! Heaps of toys and the most incredible dressing-up clothes – we're going to look fantastic at the fancy dress parade! All we need now is a rope and a bucket, and we should be able to pull it up to safety.'

'Nell brought a whole bag of skipping ropes with her,' remembered Rosanna. Amy and I will pop up and get them. The girls raced across the cave, clambered up the stone steps and poked their heads above the trap door. 'Nell!' yelled Rosanna, 'Skipping rope alert!

There was no reply. Against the door at the back of the laundry, were twelve very frightened-looking children, while advancing on them were four sinister figures in old-fashioned clothes, one of them leading a growling dog. The ghosts of the

Horrible Horde of Hyde? – or maybe there was a simpler explanation...

To the amazement of Nell's terrified gang, Rosanna and Amy launched themselves at the ghosts and toppled them to the ground.

'Show us your feet!' demanded Amy

'Why should we?' came the strangely childish voice of one of the ghosts.

'Because... you made fantastically clear footprints in the mud,' said Rosanna, 'and Amy noticed that you had crocs just like hers. Size 8-9. In our experience, ghosts don't usually wear crocs in children's sizes. Or, in fact, in any sizes, since they weren't actually invented when the Horrible Horde was at large round here.'

'Hmmm. Good point, well made,' said the kid from Arthur Road – the one who had been up the tree in the King Alfred pub the previous evening – removing her wig and shawl. 'What do you think of our outfits for the fancy dress parade, though? Wicked, aren't they!

And I'm delighted to say, that after their unmasking, the Arthur Road gang were immensely helpful, fetching buckets from St Bede School to haul up the loot from the well, and even sprinting over to the Edington Road allotments for a couple of wheelbarrows to cart it all home in – though of course, Florence managed to carry a good deal of it on her chariot as well.

Part 5: The Street Party

Despite weeks of intense preparation, the street party had got off to a slow start. There was a desultory smattering of adults, shuffling their feet and looking a bit embarrassed, but the street was completely devoid of children.The organizers were beginning to panic. The country dance band had arrived, and the fancy dress parade started in five minutes, but with only two grown-ups in costume it was going to be a wash-out. Where were the Kids of Egbert Road? The older people on the street were beginning to mutter, 'the youth of today... very badly brought up… no discipline at all… no sense of community… not like when we were young… '

Suddenly, on the wind, came the sound of a marching band: a drum beat, the squeak of a tin whistle, the silvery chime of a triangle. Led by Florence in her chariot, came a gaggle of children, all dressed in the most amazing, elaborate costumes, as well as the cheerleaders and the Spidermen who had left the pub garden earlier that morning, there were now knights, pirates, and princesses, ancient Britons, Vikings and Roman soldiers. Two of the children pushed wheelbarrows piled high with toys – heaps of beautiful old-fashioned toys. There were building bricks, hoops and sticks, toy trains, teddy bears and dolls. The older people on the street moved a little closer. These looked like the toys they had played with in their childhood. The toys that had disappeared before the Horrible Horde of Hyde were caught by the Wise Women and thrown into jail. The toys that had never been found.

With a sob, Mrs Abbot raced forward. 'My doll!' she cried, 'I'd know her anywhere!' and she plucked a beautiful china doll with blonde ringlets from the top of the wheelbarrow and threw her arms around her. And at this, all the other Hyde residents, who had been children in the days of the Horrible Horde, descended on Egbert Road, discovering their lost treasures with whoops of excitement, as the band started to play.

The Street Party held that day was the best one in living memory, as young and old from Egbert Road and all the streets around, shared toys and stories, and danced together until late into the summer evening.

Caroline Owen Wintersgill originally wrote this story to read aloud at the Egbert Road Street Party in July 2009. All the children living in the street at the time are mentioned by name, though several more have arrived since!

Street Party

by Nicky Morris

'Morning, Terry. Oh, it's not going to be the same when you retire - don't go. D'you think it's a trouser day or skirt day, Terry?'

Lily Allen's *The Fear* competed with the sound of rain outside.

'I wish you'd pronounce your T's, Lily.'

Sheila liked the rain. Hearing it dancing on the rooftop and the windowpanes, knowing she was snug inside. Another good reason to stay indoors. It helped her choose a warm fleecy top and black running bottoms, not that she had any intention of running anywhere.

'Morning, Jeannie,' she sang to the photo of her daughter, blowing it a kiss, as she drew the downstairs curtains. 'And what are you up to today? Are you out in this rain? I hope not.'

The radio kept her company all through her bowl of All Bran and marmite toast. Then she started the Independent's crossword, allowing herself half an hour. She'd only twice finished it in that time. A wash load on the thirty degrees cycle, a flick of a duster, and she was ready to settle at the computer. Friends Reunited, YouTube, My Space, Facebook, blogs, twitters, photos from all the papers; anything with pictures of people. Her eyes roamed every square inch of screen.

Lunchtime passed her by completely and it was around five when she noticed she was hungry. That would give her time to put away the Tesco Home Delivery that was due any minute, sort herself out some tea and settle down to eat it with Egg-heads. Tonight it was a team from Gateshead – called themselves 'Angels of the North' – social workers. One of them had the same colour hair as Jeannie. Same age, too. She looked at her carefully. What a lovely smile. A social worker was a worthy profession. She could see Jeannie helping others like that.

51

Egghead Kevin was chosen for the Food and Drink round. She knew that was his least favourite. His Auntie Pam lived at the end of the road and every now and then she'd pop in to share titbits. Kevin himself often passed by on his way from visiting his aunt, heading towards the pub at the other end of the road. The King Alfred. Sheila hadn't been in there for years. She was tempted, just to look at the faces, but she didn't like crowded places. She could hear the children in the garden. Sounded like a crèche.

'Oh, come on, Kevin, the answer's tea! Go with your first instinct. Rooibos redbush tea was what they drank in the The No.1 Ladies' Detective Agency. Stop wavering...'

As the phone rang, she turned down the volume but kept her eyes on the screen.

'Hello, Greg... Fine, thanks... And you?... Rain for most of the day ... You, too?... Cleared up now... No, thanks - you know I need to stay in... Yes, I've been on the rowing machine and the steps (if he could see down the phone, he'd assume her lying-induced blush was a healthy glow from all that exercise) ... Anyway, Greg, thanks for calling but I can't stay on the phone - Jeannie might ring... Yes... Right... Bye.'

And then, very shortly afterwards, bang in the middle of the final round, there was the doorbell. Scattering orange peel onto the floor, she sprinted down the hall. A woman stood in the open doorway, the evening sun behind her. Sheila's heart trampolined as she stared into her eyes. They were so familiar.

Taking a deep breath, she listened to what she was saying, having missed the first couple of sentences.

'So, I thought it would be a good idea if I delivered the invitations in person, in case you've got any questions or want more details.'

'Oh, right, thank you. Questions about what, did you say?'

'The Big Lunch invitation. See, it's on the paper.'

Sheila realised she had a piece of A4 paper in her hand, but couldn't recall how it got there. MONKS RD stood out in large letters at the top. It looked like a photograph. A photo of the road's name plaque that was on the wall of number one.

'I'm sorry, what did you say this Big Lunch was?' Sheila recognised her now. Liz from the pub end of the road. Black dog. Walked it morning and evening.

'It's an idea generated by The Eden Project,' Liz said. 'They're suggesting that everyone in the country celebrates by sharing a Big Lunch on 19th July. It's about bringing communities together. So, we're having a street party in Monks Road. We're going to fetch out tables and chairs, put up the bunting; you know, like The Queen's Jubilees. It'll be... '

Sheila's heart seemed to have stopped beating. And then it over compensated, pumping so quickly and so loudly that it drowned everything out. She couldn't breathe.

'Are you all right?' Liz asked. 'Can I get you a glass of water or something?' But the voice was coming from miles away. Somehow, she managed to close the door and find her way back to the safety of her sofa.

***

Reaching the end of the road, Liz, now relieved of all the invitations, arrived at Pam's door. Worried, she told her of Sheila's funny turn. Over cups of tea, Pam explained.

'It was the Queen's Silver Jubilee when it happened. A beautiful sunny day. Street looked grand. All the neighbours turned out. We borrowed the parish hall tables and stretched them down the middle of the road. Someone had got rolls of Union Jack wrapping paper so we covered them with that but you couldn't see it for the mountain of jellies and cakes – all red, white and blue. There were sandwiches, too, and sausage rolls; proper party food. We had big speakers up one end playing the music. Lots of patriotic tunes – Jerusalem, Land of Hope and Glory – that sort of thing. And there were balloons and flags and streamers all over the place. Oh – and the bunting – every house had bunting stretching from one side to the other. It was

53

magnificent. And everyone was so jolly. It was a really happy, sunshiny day until Jeannie went missing.

Poor Sheila and Greg. They were frantic. We all thought they were panicking over nothing at first but then when we realised it was serious, everyone joined in with the hunt. Some of the kids had wandered into the park. They could remember Jeannie being with them but no one could actually recall her coming back up the steps with them into the road. The police were called in and all the houses were searched, top to bottom. They combed the park, rivers as well, and then the whole of Winchester - but not a trace of her. Except for one little yellow wellington boot from her Paddington Bear. He went everywhere with her. They found it at the far end of the park, near the Art School. And all the children swore they hadn't gone that far.

Dreadful it was, absolutely dreadful. Greg went out searching, day after day. But Sheila wouldn't leave the house, always hopeful Jeannie would turn up on the doorstep. She never did. It's over thirty years she's been waiting now. All alone in her house – but she won't give up hope. It all got too much for Greg. He tried to move her on but the strain must have been terrible. They divorced about ten years after it happened. We never see him any more.

I expect it was you talking of Street Parties got her in a bit of a lather. But don't go worrying yourself. The world's got to carry on.'

***

And it did. As July approached, all round Britain, neighbours formed committees to organise parties. Councils gave permission for street closures. Village halls were booked, recreation grounds advertised family sports events; activities of every type flourished. A buzz was in the air from Lands End to John o' Groats. And bang in the middle, a road in a small town on the outskirts of Birmingham was preparing for the big event, too.

Jane and her son were visiting her mother especially for the street party. All the previous day they'd baked cup cakes, icing them in bright pink goo and covering them in 100s and 1000s.

'It's meant to be healthy home-grown food,' Jane said. 'Not this e-number monster mush. You'll be as jumpy as a grasshopper by midday.'

'Ah, leave him be, love,' her mother said. 'A bit of hyper never hurt anyone.'

But it was Jane who was feeling out of sorts by the following afternoon. Leaving the house, it was like stepping onto a stage set. She was shy at first, then as the cava corks popped, more and more people came to introduce themselves. Even so, she couldn't settle. Something wasn't right. The bunting – the music – the long line of tables – garden chairs. It felt like a play in which she had to act but she'd lost her script.

'Mummy, Mummy, can I have my face painted? Gran says to come down the road to watch me. What shall I be – a king or a tiger?'

He tugged Jane towards the gaggle of children circling the face-painters. Most of the adults had taken advantage and slipped to the end of the road where they'd created a bar, consequently there were spare chairs, so she plonked herself down opposite her mother. Over her shoulder she stared into a curtainless window, attracted by the bright room within. All the walls – even the ceiling – were painted in sunshine. And on top of a yellow filing cabinet, sat a huge yellow Wellington boot made out of pottery. Jane felt as if it had lifted itself up and kicked her in the stomach.

A stage set more vivid than the one she was now in flashed back: louder music, brighter light, more people, stronger smells. Children the same size as her, adults in the distance. And Paddington. Her Paddington with both his yellow wellies. As a four year-old, she'd cried not because she'd lost her identity, but because Paddington had lost one of his boots.

In panic, Jane looked for her son, who was standing nearby, beaming through a stripy face. She pulled him to her and held on for dear life.

Then she looked at the woman who sat opposite and said, 'You're not my real mother, are you?'

***

Liz stood back and surveyed the scene in Monks Road with satisfaction. It couldn't have looked more festive. All the cars had been moved, the entrance to the park blocked off, the road closed at the pub end. Their own little community with everyone happy - and the sun shining. Pam had even tempted Sheila out of her house. And there she was now, with a smile as wide as any of the children's.

Sheila wasn't quite sure what had happened but something had. The knot in her stomach that had been tied for thirty-two years had untangled itself.

Jeannie was coming home. She just knew she was.

Nicky Morris lives in Monks Road and is one of the instigators of the Hyde900 'Bring-Your-Own- Literature' evenings held monthly in the Hyde Tavern.

Sepia: a Poem of Old Hyde

by Kevin Barrett

Old memories musty like second hand clothes
at a Parish jumble sale.
The percussion of industry melts into sepia streets,
dark shapes indistinct move through mists,
leaves bob and weave in Autumnal breeze,
the November evening cold and black trembles
while bonfires burn.
Calloused hands knap ancient flint,
while shadows dance upon yellow stone.
And into darkening reed beds ghosts disappear.

Reflections in a Park

by Kevin Barrett

The old corner shop, boats on the river,
Mums, dads, ice cream cones, a spent arrow from time's
quiver.
Circuses, funfairs, grans, and aunts
Golden memories that still enchants.
The putting green and soda pop
All gone now like the corner shop.
Summer evenings, uncles and cricket matches long forgot.
And the mother looks at the new born baby in her cot.

Kevin Barrett, from Stanmore, is part of the Hyde900 Bring-Your-Own-Literature group.

The Tale of Winnall Moors

by Ross Humphrys

Chapter One

Dominic inched slowly across the narrow, rickety bridge, just above a river full of ferocious Jimblams. They had a taste for blood, as Dominic's scrape was dripping into the river. As he inched, Dominic wondered how he had got into this mess. He couldn't remember, even though it was yesterday, although under the circumstances that was acceptable. It had started with Alfred's announcement.

'Shut up!' Alfred had yelled, banging his royal mushroom. 'This is important!'

Silence stampeded like a bull around the Great Hall.

'The book of secrets must be recovered!' shouted Gawain. This elf was in charge of King Alfred's army, and his personal assistant in battle. 'It contains everything the Vikings need to destroy our community of elfish harmony forever! As you all know, they sent this scumbag,' he glared at the spy, chained in front of the judge, 'to steal it for them. He succeeded, but our armies tracked him to the heart of the abandoned forest. He heard us coming, and hid the book somewhere there. It must be found!'

'But,' put in Alfred, 'who by? I cannot go. Gawain claims he must stay with his soldiers. And the other generals are off slaying a Clonk. So – who will go?'

The Great Hall fell silent. Nobody wanted to go – they all knew it was going to be extremely dangerous. Dominic, sitting unnoticed in the middle of the crowd, observed and noted this. He sighed and spoke up.

'I could do it,' he mumbled. All eyes in the Great Hall turned to stare at him. Slowly, a ripple of laughter spread out. Dominic was not well known for either his status as a mere legionary or his fighting skills. And then, something unexpected happened.

'Yes, let him go,' spoke up Gawain. 'It will leave our best remaining soldiers to guard the spy.'

This time, amazement rippled out from Gawain. Dominic recognised the insult, but that didn't matter. He ran to the front, the crowd parting as he went. A slightly dazed Alfred handed Dominic a piece of parchment, which he recognised as a map of the Winnall Moors. He ran back, the crowd again parting. He burst out of the Great Hall doors, and bolted for the safety of the moors. Dominic knew he would never stop until the book was recovered!

Chapter Two

Twenty metres in, Dominic was starting to think this wasn't such a good idea. Nevertheless, his community was in deadly peril, and he would do whatever he could to save it. Another thirty metres and Dominic sank onto a small toadstool for a rest. The thrill of being allowed to go was fading and he was beginning to worry. Also, as he looked up, he noticed something. Or didn't notice something. The clearing he was in was so dark, and gloomy, that he could barely see three inches forward. The moors were thriving with unknown creatures, and everywhere around him welcomed danger.

As he struggled to make sense of his surroundings, Dominic began to feel a sense of déjà vu. The feeling was confirmed when a flock of silent, swift Blonghafs swooped overhead, one of them catching a claw on the map, tugging it from Dominic's grip. Dominic shouted loudly, leapt to his feet, and raced after the retreating flock. Many times he nearly lost sight of them, and he was horrified to think that he might have failed King Alfred within the first five minutes of his quest. But eventually, Dominic saw the map fall. He charged towards it – and skidded to a halt. The map had fallen on the opposite bank of an impossibly deep river. Dominic had gained a scrape from pursuing the Blonghafs, and blood was dripping into the river. And frothing up the muddy, cloudy water were at least twenty of the largest, scaliest, ferocious-looking Jimblams ever.

'Oh, great,' muttered Dominic.

He contemplated how to get across. There were no nearby vines, and he hadn't brought a rope. He looked around. that was when he noticed the bridge. But there was one problem … it was the ricketiest, weakest-looking, most unreliable bridge Dominic had ever seen. On the other hand, it was the only possible way across. And there he was, inching across the bridge towards the map.

'OK Dominic, be careful,' Dominic muttered to himself. 'One wrong move could upset this whole bridge.'

And, of course, the very next thing that happened was that Dominic balanced his weight on the wrong foot, the bridge's already weak supports snapped, Dominic was thrown forwards, and after two seconds of agonising terror, found himself clutching for dear life to one half of the bridge as it dangled over the overwhelming gorge of the river. For about two minutes, two, terrifying, blood-curdling minutes, Dominic just hung, like an anxious spider. He was roused from his relief when he noticed that a peckish Jimblam was nibbling his heel. Scrambling frantically up the ladder gave Dominic a sense of hyperactivity, so when he reached the safety of the high ground, it took him a moment to notice the scrap of parchment fluttering in his face.

'The map!' Dominic laughed. He snatched it up, dusted it off and shoved it in a cavernous pocket. Until now, it was just being out here actually doing something that had kept him going. However, he now felt that he could actually do this. He was going to show those people back home who the brave one was around there!

Thinking these happy thoughts, Dominic plunged once more onto the path of adventure. Unknowingly, though, he was heading towards the biggest revelation of his life.

Chapter Three

Dominic tiptoed between the dark trees. About ten minutes ago, he had noticed the map was vibrating. He took it out and consulted it. A large, dominating **X** had appeared, and no less than half a centimetre away from it was a tiny, half-invisible dot labelled 'Dominic.' Now, he glanced at it for the third time since discovering the **X**. His little dot was now approximately a millimetre from the **X**, and the map was vibrating harder than ever.

Suddenly, Dominic felt warmth on the back of his neck. He looked up. He had emerged into a clearing, with sunlight streaming through a gap in the trees overhead. Abruptly, the map hissed. Dominic jumped a foot in the air, and gazed at it. An arrow had now appeared, over the whole page, with a small caption underneath. Dominic read it:

'He who seeks the book of secrets need only follow the path this arrow carves, and he will have the knowledge that his heart is brave and true, and his people will know him as the saviour of their kingdom.'

Dominic's eyes lit up – he would be respected at last! He peered at the arrow – straight forward, it said. Dominic did so, until it hissed again. He studied it – now it told him to turn left, and keep going until he reached a rhubarb bush. Again, he did so, and as he approached the rhubarb bush, the map began to growl. Dominic's whole body tingled. The book of secrets was merely inches away! Heart hammering, he pushed aside some leaves, and there, nestled in a small hole, was …

'The book!' Dominic whispered.

All of a sudden, Dominic realised that some unknown force was reeling in his hand, and before he had fully grasped this, he was holding the book.

The map screamed happily, and exploded in a puff of sparkly blue smoke. As he breathed it in, Dominic felt something happening. It was like his whole body was rippling, but when he looked down at himself there was nothing. And then it was over. Dominic could feel some sort of power flowing through him. It made him want to yell, to shout to the world that here was a new Dominic, ready to take on any task thrown at him. But just as he was about to do so, he heard someone clapping. Then a bored drawl.

'Oh yes, very good. Congratulations, whoopee, hooray, etc.'

And to Dominic's immense and utter shock, Commander Gawain stepped into the clearing.

Chapter Four

'I see you've found the book,' Gawain's voice was hard and cold. 'Just as I hoped. This'll make things easy.'

'Wh – wh – what are you doing here?!' Dominic stuttered. 'I mean – how - ?'

'Oh, the usual,' Gawain answered. 'Kill you, take the book, betray Alfred, allow the Vikings to take over Hyde. That's about it.'

'B – but – why?'

A few moments silence, and then –

'Alfred doesn't pay me anything!' Gawain snarled. 'Never! But the Vikings promised me cash! Lots of it! All I had to do was give them the book of secrets. I couldn't be seen stealing it, so I hired a Viking soldier to steal it for me. I waited for him here, and when he arrived, the army hot on his heels, he gave it to me, and while he got himself captured, I hid the book here, to collect later. But then Alfred insisted on sending out a search!'

He ground his teeth. 'I had no choice.'

Dominic was trying to understand a lot of things at the moment. For one, why was Gawain telling him all this? And then, he had the answer. It was all right for him to know, because – Dominic gulped – he wasn't going to live to tell anyone else. Still only barely comprehending, he enquired, 'So...why did you let me go?'

'To give me an easy finish.' Gawain advanced on Dominic. 'Here is where it ends...'

Dominic retreated to the edge of the clearing, Gawain following him all the time. Eventually, they reached a tree that was as solid as a cliff face. Dominic wasn't expecting to hit a tree, so when his spine slammed into it, he naturally dropped the book. And, by an amazing amount of luck, it fell open at just the right page. Now, you have to remember that this was a book of secrets. That's all well and good, but it didn't just contain secrets about Hyde. It also held all there was to know about the old ways, of magic and warlocks and witches, and the page the book had fallen open at, completely visible to Dominic, was a page on transportation. The title on the page caught Dominic's attention, and reading through the page in a matter of seconds (the powers Dominic had gained from the book somehow enabled him to do this) he saw a path out of his predicament. Putting into account all that he had read, Dominic muttered something in Arabic-sounding words, whistled and disappeared in a haze of steam, leaving a terrified, yet puzzled Gawain, behind in the forest. But not before he had reached down and snatched up the book.

Chapter Five

Dominic whirled round like a top, blinded by a spinning vortex of colour. The wind whistling in his ears was deafening, and the book was beginning to slip from his grasp. However, just as Dominic relinquished his grip on the book, his feet slammed into solid ground.

Dominic stumbled; the book clattered into the corner of wherever he was as Dominic sank to his knees. His vision was still streaked with colour, so it took him a moment to register exactly where he was – when he realised, he leapt to his feet with a whoop of triumph. He was back in the Great Hall where this disastrous journey had begun.

It was now completely empty, of course – but outside, Dominic could hear the hustle and bustle of his fellow elves going about their daily lives. And in the distance, Dominic could hear – very faintly – the boom of King Alfred's voice bellowing at one of his servants. Seizing the book as he ran, Dominic dashed down the room and burst out into the happy, smiling sunlight. At first no-one noticed him, but as he tore through them, some elves recognised him. And a bit further on, they realised what he was carrying.

A massive cheer rose up from the street as Dominic charged up the glittering marble steps of King Alfred's palace. His royal dining room was not far from the oak front doors, so seconds later, Dominic sprinted in.

A gasp rose up from Alfred and his servants as Dominic strode towards the King. When he reached him, Dominic bowed, kneeled, and presented the book of secrets to an astonished Alfred.

'I bring you the book, Your Majesty, Dominic murmured.

King Alfred stared at the book. Slowly, he reached out. Picking up the book tenderly, he examined it from all sides, as if checking whether it was a fake. Then he went mad.

'Congratulations, my boy! A celebration is called for! We must get to work! COOK!!' he roared. Cook jumped, and hurried forwards. 'Prepare a royal feast in honour of our friend and saviour Dominic here!' Alfred shouted, quieter as Cook was closer.

'Certainly, my lord!' squeaked Cook as he scurried away.

'Sir, I have bad news,' said Dominic, as Cook vanished through the door, and he filled Alfred in on the disloyalty of Gawain. Alfred frowned.

'I never did trust him,' he grumbled. 'He was always reluctant to fight. I'll send out an armed squad. But,' he rumbled, brightening, 'mustn't forget that feast, eh, boy?' Alfred beamed. 'You're a hero! And that's just for starters! I think you've more than earned the right to the title of Mayor of all Winchester! How's that for a reward, eh?'

Dominic beamed back. He had waited his whole life for this, and the moment was finally here. But then he remembered something.

'Sir,' he said thoughtfully, 'don't you think the Vikings will want revenge after this?'

'Drat.' Alfred sounded annoyed. 'Well, I wouldn't put it past them. Yes, I suppose so. But until then, let's enjoy that feast. Yes?'

Dominic considered. It would be a while until the Vikings discovered that Gawain had failed. They would definitely come after it. But, Dominic remembered, he had control over the book and its powers. The Vikings wanted the book? They would have to get past him first. And he would be ready.

'Yes,' said Dominic, and grinned.

THE END...FOR NOW!

Ross Humphrys from Monks Road has lived in Winchester for 10 years and is a pupil at Westgate School.

Hyde Church Hall

by Lynda O'Neill

Kind Mr Barratt drove my darlings to Sunday School
for their transient wrestle with faith. It must have been fun
or they wouldn't have gone, those eighties children.
So different to my colouring-in of shepherds and disciples,
reverent page turning of Edwardian books with
a soppy-faced Jesus and money changers in the temple.

In my slimming club years the hall smelt musty;
paint peeled, radiators roared like the fires of hell.
Weighed in weekly, praised for half a pound's loss,
did they believe us when we swore that
pasties or Mars Bars never sullied our fridges?
The leader, so slim we wanted to smack her,
laid on a feast as reward, aggrieved we left her
exhausted vol-au-vents, a squashed tomato.

Refurbished, refurnished, it gleams after
dogged fund raising. Now I read my poems there.
Glad of the laughter of recognition, I recall
how the sixties didn't swing for me,
the English teacher with gin in her handbag,
the blessed memory of Nan taking me to Cinderella,
thrilled when David Scott listens and praises.

Lynda O'Neill, who lives in Fulflood, is a poet.

An Honourable and Patriotic Life

by Len Ruffell

One of the most impressive events held at Hyde took place at St Bartholomew's Church one Tuesday afternoon in September 1932. It was the funeral service for James William Ruffell, formerly a Chief Petty Officer in the Royal Navy who had seen action in the First World War. His coffin, draped with the Union Jack and bearing his medals, was carried by a guard of honour of six Petty Officers in uniform under a Naval Commander. Admiral Dicken was present, along with civic dignitaries, military personnel, magistrates, Winchester College staff, local employers and representatives of the British Legion. They joined family, friends and neighbours to pay tribute to this remarkable man who had grown up in the parish.

His body was borne to West Hill Cemetery where many beautiful floral tokens were laid. One stood out. It was from Admiral Dicken and carried the message: "A tribute to an honourable and patriotic life". It was a mark of respect from one distinguished seaman to another. Yet few who stood at the graveside would be aware of the tough start James had in life. He was the sort of man who spoke only about the good days, never the hard times.

The story really begins with his father, Henry Ruffell, who came to live in Hyde in 1855. Queen Victoria was on the throne and Henry, or Harry as he was called, was 30 and full of optimism. Born in the village of Bighton, he had been an ostler at the Queen's Head, Alton, until he moved to stay with his sister, Elizabeth, and her husband George Young and their children in Hyde Church Yard.

Harry had no difficulty obtaining employment as a groom at one of the many coaching inns which thrived in Winchester. A good looking man, he found himself attracted to a serving girl, Louisa Burden from Gillingham, Dorset. They fell in love and it was not long before Harry moved from stable groom to bride-groom. On 16 April 1859 they were married. They did not have far to walk for the ceremony. It took place at St Bartholomew's Church, which was virtually next door to the house they lived in.

Harry became a gardener and jobs took them to live for a while in Great Minster Street and St John's Terrace but at the first opportunity they returned to live in Hyde. They had been married 8 years and Harry was doing well. He and Louisa were happy with four healthy children and a comfortable home in Hyde Close. Then, out of the blue, tragedy struck. In June 1867 Louisa became ill. She was rushed to the County Hospital doubled up and in great pain. Tragically, it was too late. She was suffering from cancer of the stomach and the liver. It was in an advanced state and there was nothing doctors could do. She died. She was just 41 and her youngest child, Phoebe, was under a year old.

Heartbroken, Harry wondered how he could cope with four children on his own. The youngest was a babe in arms. The eldest, James, was only 7. Harry could afford to employ a housekeeper but even so, life became an endless struggle. In the end it was just too much and a year later, he died unexpectedly. Harry was 44 and the death had to be investigated by the coroner. Charles Dickens could not have described the pathetic scene better than this report in the Hampshire Chronicle of 16 February 1868.

> *An inquest was held yesterday before Mr J H Todd, Coroner, on the body of Henry Ruffell, widower. It appears that deceased, with his four children, resided in Hyde Close, and the latter were tended by a woman who acted in the capacity of housekeeper. Ruffell retired to rest in the enjoyment of good health on Wednesday evening, but as he did not make his appearance at the usual hour next morning, his housekeeper went to his room, where she found his children endeavouring*

to awake him. He was, however, dead, and the body nearly cold. At the conclusion of the evidence, the jury returned a verdict of "Visitation of God".

Harry had, in today's terms, suffered a cardiac arrest but his friends said he died of a broken heart. Arrangements were made for the funeral. Burials no longer took place in the Churchyard adjoining his home. That practice had ceased 12 years earlier, and instead his body was taken, as Louisa's had before him, to the new public cemetery at West Hill. In the St Bartholomew's Church Journal, Rev W Williams, Vicar, recorded conducting the funeral the following Sunday afternoon at 4 o'clock. It is likely that James, the eldest child, who was 7 was there. If so, he would have been old enough to ponder the fate which might await him and his siblings as they entered life in the orphanage.

James had a distinctive feature that made him stand out from the crowd. Unusually, nature had endowed him with one blue eye and one brown. When he was 10, a vacancy occurred at Christe's Hospital, after a boy named Henry Sims left to take up an apprenticeship. The ancient charitable institution, situated near Winchester Cathedral, provided accommodation for six old men and four poor boys. The Churchwardens of St Bartholomew's were quick to put forward the name of James William Ruffell. It was a great opportunity.

Unfortunately, although a bright pupil, James did not take well to life at Christe's Hospital. He was a spirited boy and the records show he often had to be disciplined. In June 1872 a report on the conduct of the Boy Ruffell was submitted to the charity's Conservator and Gubarnators. It said he had been frequently admonished and punished and was, they concluded, incorrigible. Accordingly, they expelled him. He was returned to the responsibility of the Overseers of the Winchester Union and the Churchwardens of St Bartholomew's Parish.

He was now 13½ and old enough to go to work. Over the next eighteen months, numerous attempts were made to find suitable employment for him. The Board found benevolent employers willing to give him a chance. They included Mr Forder M.O. in St Thomas's Parish and Mr Shrimpton at Bishopstoke. But it was hopeless. He never settled anywhere. It was, no doubt, with a sense of relief that the exasperated authorities discovered, one day in April 1875, that the boy had run away to sea.

Joining the Royal Navy gave James the fresh start he needed. It was to prove the best move he ever made. He was 15 and he loved life aboard ship. Trained as a gunner, he sailed across the world helping to keep the Pax Britannica. His travels took him to the exotic seaports of the Far East. In Japan, he had his boson's whistle engraved "Nagasaki" as a souvenir. At Hong Kong, China, then a major trading port of the British Empire, he had his photograph taken. Every time he returned on leave he made his way back to his old friends in Hyde Churchyard Lane. Voyages were long in those days and there were months, sometimes years, between visits but no one could fail to notice the insignia on his uniform. It showed a steady rise in rank.

James took advantage of the educational opportunities the Navy provided and at 28, he was a Chief Petty Officer. They say all the nice girls love a sailor but his greatest admirer was his long time sweetheart, Elizabeth Lovelock. She lived in Hyde, where her father was a maltster at the brewery. From the moment she saw James in his uniform, she fell for him. They were often apart but he wrote frequently to her on his voyages aboard Her Majesty's Ships Shah, Liffey, Triumph and Penguin. He popped the question and James' name re-appears in the St Bartholomew Church register when on 9 January 1888, he and Elizabeth were married. It was 15 years after he had left the parish to go to sea.

They set up home at 10 Hyde Close, which they shared with Elizabeth's brother, George Lovelock, a baker, and his wife Kate.

Elizabeth had their first child, a son christened William Stanley Ruffell, there in 1892. By the time their next child who, unfortunately, did not survive infancy, was born in 1901 James had retired from the Navy. He had received the Long Service and Good Conduct medal and had risen to the highest non-commissioned rank in the Royal Navy, that of Chief Quartermaster.

He had a good Naval pension and they went to live at 21 King Alfred Place where another child, Violet was born in 1904. James was still in his 40s and he did not settle easily into civilian life. His skills in seamanship did not equip him for many jobs ashore in Winchester but he was not afraid of hard work. He obtained employment as a fitter at the Vulcan Ironworks in Kings Worthy. Timesheets in the archives at Hampshire Record Office show that he sometimes worked a 57 hour week.

When the Great War broke out in August 1914, the Royal Navy needed experienced seamen. Although he was 54, James immediately volunteered for active service. He was posted to the China Station where he joined the battleship, HMS Kent. He was the oldest sailor on board. He did not have to wait long to see action. In December, a wireless message was received that a German Squadron, including four fast, modern light cruisers was menacing the sea lanes of the South Atlantic. The Kent was among the British ships sent to hunt down and destroy them.

They sighted the Kaiser's ships off the Falkland Islands. The SMS Nurnberg opened the firing and the Kent sustained some damage. But by drawing the German's fire, the crew on the British vessel could gauge its range. The highly trained Royal Navy gunners were the best in the world and they let fly with all the power their guns could muster. From a distance of 6½ miles their first shell struck the Nurnberg square in the stern. She was sunk - one of three German cruisers sent to the bottom by the British Fleet.

Only SMS Dresden got away and the Kent joined the hunt for her. They spent weeks chasing the Dresden until they cornered her at the Robinson Crusoe island of San Juan Fernandez, off the coast of Chile. The sight of the Kent and HMS Glasgow was enough for the German crew and rather than see her captured, they scuttled their ship. On return to England, Chief Petty Officer Ruffell received prize money for the action. Later he left the Kent and was transferred to HMS Dolphin where he served until the end of the war.

After such adventure, it was with some reluctance that James left life at sea for the last time. A friendly and gregarious man, he was a popular figure in Hyde. He involved himself in the community, being a keen gardener and an active supporter of the British Legion. He worked on and off at Winchester College, where he was an inspiration to staff and pupils alike. Sadly, when he was 70, he suffered a stroke and never fully recovered. He hung on until 16th September 1932 when he died peacefully at home in King Alfred Place, just a short distance from the house in Hyde where the dramatic events which shaped his path in life had occurred.

Len Ruffell lives in Harestock and is Chairman of the Hampshire Genealogical Society.

Still Life in Hyde

by Richard Stillman

I am a still life: old woman at window
trying to play snap with my memory,
conscious of being hunched, a poorhouse widow,
tired of playing my role in the story.

Trying to play snap with my memory
I suffer my daughter, fussing around
and though tired of playing my role in the story,
I say, 'Thank you,' keeping the rest deep down.

I suffer my daughter, fussing around,
another cup of tea, another pale debt paid.
I say, 'Thank you,' keeping the rest deep down.
If words are hateful, they're better left unsaid

Another cup of tea, another pale debt paid
Did I say, 'Thank you,' with enough grace?
If words are hateful, they're better left unsaid,
I mutter my words, that being the case.

Did I say, 'Thank you,' with enough grace?
Will she tell on me, and say I'm not all there?
I mutter my words, that being the case.
Say all you like, dear, and see if I care.

Will she tell on me, and say I'm not all there?
Tell him how ungrateful I am to be here.
Say all you like, dear, and see if I care.
I'll just moulder away in your comfortable chair.

Tell him how ungrateful I am to be here,
this slow dying wearies my cold soul.
I'll just moulder away in your comfortable chair
until you weary too, and feel old, old.

This slow dying wearies my cold soul
conscious of being hunched, a poorhouse widow
until you weary too, and feel old, old,
I am a still life: old woman at window.

Richard is Head of English Literature at Peter Symonds College and a member of the Hyde Tavern Writers' group.

Letter to Uncle Nigel, 2159

by Joe Bayles

Hi Uncle Nigel,

I hope you are well. I've been really busy at school. This week we're doing a project about school children 150 years ago. They were really worried about the earth heating up and called it Global Warming. The world did get warmer for about 20 years, but then the big freeze came. We've had a fun week here.

On Tuesday Dad crashed the snowmobile into the giant Hyde1000 King Alfred statue. We had to go to St Bede on our cross country skis.

On Wednesday we did Sports Day practice. We did ice skating on the River Itchen in the park. I nearly skated into a Penguin. Harry is lucky because he can practice skating outside our house on Arthur Road.

We had an exciting day on Friday. A polar bear escaped from the nature reserve, and it was finally caught in the Riverside Nursery.

The Talks family on Saxon Road have got a super hovercraft snowmobile. It's really cool and I hope that we can get one soon.

I hope it's not too cold in Australia.

Love

Joe.

Joe Bayles is a pupil at St Bede.

Ode To Hyde Tavern Ghost

by Hannah Jenkins

The story goes or so it is said
In the Hyde Tavern Pub
A pilgrim lady begged for a bed.

For food and shelter on a cold winter night
Being refused, she suffered to its might

Found on the doorstep
She now comes to haunt.

Taking bed covers from those in these beds

Never seen, Never heard
The guests of today are often disturbed…

Hannah Jenkins is a pupil at St Bede.

The Hyde Tavern Ghost

a play by Rachel O'Neill

The action is set in Hyde in the autumn of 1110.

Interior: Small, bare room. A young girl sits by a hearth.

Soldier: (offstage) Get in there! Ow! She bit!

Captain: Now, now, what would our Lord say about biting?

The door opens and another girl, Mathilda, dressed as a postulant is thrown into the room.

Captain: Now get in, you English cow !

Mathilda: Don't dare to talk to me of the Lord. You leave him out of it, you norman swine!

A man enters. He is an army captain in his 40s.

Captain: Give me any more trouble and I'll take you right back to the Nunnaminster. Now stay there and shut up and behave.

Anne: Who are you? Why are you in my house?

Captain: Sorry for bursting in on you unannounced. Me and my men are doing a house-to-house search and this little cat was not helping. Do you mind if I leave her here for a while? We'll be back later. You mind your manners. *(He leaves).*

Mathilda: French cochon!

Captain re-enters.

Captain: I was born in Alresford, actually. *(Exits)*

Anne: Errm. Are you all right?

Mathilda: Me? I'm fine. Just a couple of bruises. He's a right ...

Anne: *(quickly)* Are you a nun then?

Mathilda: Yes, I bloomin' well am.

Anne: You don't seem very like a nun to me.

Mathilda: Well I am. At least I'm an apprentice nun. Don't look at me like that. We get three meals a day and I don't have to fight off the cowman. There is a lot of praying though. Even for nuns there's a huge amount of praying - matins, noon and compline.

Anne: And why...? *(she gestures to the door)*

Mathilda: They came to the St Mary's early yesterday morning. They wanted gold. The Abbess refused and they threatened. Well. You can imagine what they threatened. Eventually, she agreed to unlock the chest.

Anne: But who are they? Are they mercenaries?

Mathilda: No. They are the King's men. They're legitimate all right - apart from that Norman swine.

Anne: Why did they want Abbey gold?

Mathilda: Apparently the paymaster appears to have gone missing between here and Basingstoke. Taking the pay. And the soldiers were getting restless. So you can imagine that the last thing the Bishop wants is a bunch of well-armed, unpaid soldiers roaming around Winchester.

Anne: But why are you with them?

Mathilda: Because they have left a few guards there. Guards who are going to get drunk on our honey wine. The Abbess persuaded the Captain to take me and place me somewhere safe.

Anne: But why would she do that?

Mathilda: You mean why bother? Well, you're right, I'm not one of the nobility like most of the other nuns. I don't know. Maybe she is just a good woman and she thought I might be in danger if I stayed round the Abbey. I don't actually care. This is the most exciting thing that's happened since those men came poking round, doing some kind of adding up of everything in the land so the Norman conqueror knows just how many shifts the nuns of the great Abbey of St Mary's launder each month.

Anne: Oh.

Edward enters. Soldier in his 20s.

Edward: So, which one of you is the famous biting nun? Oh, it must be you, miss. Don't try it with me. I heard about you trying to run away and the Captain restraining you. Why are you still here? Has this lass here got a bow and arrow trained on your head?

Mathilda: You know, I realised that for the first time in almost two years I'm outside the nunnery walls. I'm seeing the world! *(she looks round)* Well, a bit of the world. A small bit.

Edward: Oh, don't get on your high horse. It's dark, it's cold and this charming young lady might rustle up some soup for us if we both ask nicely.

Anne: Oh yes. I've got some on the go. No pork but plenty of beans and radishes.

Edward: And I have bread and beer so we have a feast. And what will you contribute, M'Lady Sharp Teeth?

Mathilda: When can I go home?

Edward: We're moving out at daybreak.

Anne: I thought you were doing a - what was it? - a house to house search?

Edward: Captain always says that when we need an overnight billet. The good monks up the road only have a limited number of beds. Tomorrow we're marching to Romsey. Now where's that soup?

Mathilda: And I can go back to St Mary's?

Edward: You can go tomorrow. I'll deliver you back safely. That Abbess is very protective isn't she? Didn't think much of our lads' ability to resist your charms.

Mathilda: Maybe she knows soldiers better than you do.

Edward: That may be right. I've only been a soldier since Michaelmas. I'm a novice - like you.

As they sit to eat, the Captain enters.

Captain: Right. Managed to get the men billeted. Not over friendly your Hyde neighbours. Are they all like that?

Anne: No. Only since the illness has come. No one goes out much for fear of breathing the miasma.

Captain: Soup's nice. Bit thin.

Anne: I'm sorry. I don't have much. I don't think anyone round here has planted up in time for winter. And with sons and fathers ill or dead, the Duke's fields are left to rot.

Captain: *(looking round)* Is that what's happened here?

Edward: Yes, where is the rest of your family? It's dark. Are they on their way back from the fields?

Anne: No. There's no one. Just me. *(pause).* My sister and then my mother died from the sickness.

Edward: I'm sorry.

Captain: Me too. I can't bear sad stories. They bring an unnatural amount of water to my eyes. Think I'll just step down the road to the tavern and try and get a game.

Mathilda: Wait for me! I'll get my cloak.

Captain: Hang on. I don't think your abbess would like me to take you to drink beer and play dice in some Hyde hovel.

Mathilda: Look, I'll be really quiet. In fact, you can ask the landlady if I can sit in her parlour while you play cards. It'd be cheerier than here.

Captain: *(sighs)* All right. But no biting and no cheekiness. And no flirting, it's not a good look on a nun. *(To the other)* Back in a couple of hours, bit of kip and then we'll push off at daybreak. I've told the lads to assemble by the Gate House. You need to collect the horses and whatever provisions we can get from the monks.

Edward: Yes, Sir.

Mathilda and the Captain exit.

Edward: So do you want to tell me what happened?

Anne: We were too weak, unable to fetch food and fresh water. A neighbour looked after us for a bit. And the priest from St Barnabas came by but they stopped coming. I don't know what happened to them. The worst day was when mother died. It began like the days have begun for the past two months. The clawing in your belly wakes you and your tongue's parched like shoe leather. And then the smell hits you and there is no chance of any more sleep. Since they've taken to piling the bodies up against the church, the stink creeps under the doors and through the windows. I'd been sleeping on the hearth. Since Lucy died I'd not wanted to sleep in our bed and when mother became ill I persuaded her to have it. It was still dark; the embers from last night's fire gave a pallid light to the room. Mother was still in her bed and though I'd nursed her until I was too tired to stand I could see she wouldn't need any more care. I have tried not to think of myself but to pray constantly for their immortal souls but the truth is I can't think of them in paradise with my father without wishing I was there, too.

Edward: Don't think that. I'll think you want to do yourself some harm.

Anne: I pray but it doesn't stop me being frightened.

Edward: But you have a secure house. It will keep you warm and dry over the winter.

Anne: *(Laughing)* Yes. And the rent is due St Steven's day and I don't have it. What with nursing my sister and mother, I haven't planted more than a few cabbages and some rye and I've only spun enough wool to make myself a cloak that will have to be my shelter when the Duke's bailiff turns me out. Sorry, I'm feeling a bit sorry for myself.

Edward: I didn't realise it was so bad. We heard that Winchester was a rich city, prosperous.

Anne: The cold weather spoilt the harvest and then the sickness came. Only the monks at the Abbey have not been affected. They've only been by once and that was to remove the bodies and stack them until the ground unfreezes. I don't even know if Mother and Lucy are buried yet. *(pause)*

Edward: Look. You can't stay here. Even if the sickness has gone, you won't get through the winter. Have you no friends or family?

Anne: No. We moved here from King's Somborne when father died.

Edward: That was a risk. Big town. No protector.

Anne: With all the new people coming in to work on the New Minster, we thought that the three of us could make a living. We're spinners. We didn't reckon on the sickness. Don't worry. It isn't in this house. I would have warned you otherwise.

Edward: Listen. My family live on the Romsey Road. I know that they will take you in out of charity. They have a small farm and my mother has a loom - she will be glad of your skills. If you can gather everything up you need to take, we can set off tomorrow morning after I've taken young madam back to the Abbey.

Anne: Oh! Would they? Do you think? I would be grateful to go as a servant and earn my keep.

Edward: Of course. You are honest, good, kind - I can tell that.Why should you fade away here? Sinking into the hearthstones like so much ash. My family will welcome you as one of their own. Now let's try and get some sleep. You and the young nun should sleep upstairs and the Captain and I will stretch out here.

Anne: I don't know what to say. To think that if you hadn't come by, I would be trapped here. Waiting to be turned out onto the streets with no food, no shelter. What would have happened to me?

Edward: Hush now. I have always brought home orphaned fox cubs and hedgehogs. You will be like one of those.

Anne: *(laughs)* Why, thank you. Will I be more smelly than prickly? Or,the other way round?

Edward: *(laughs)* Who knows? I'd have to give you a good sniff and a good feel... *(awkward pause)*

Anne: I'll always be in your debt. I'll be more grateful than your animal waifs and strays.

Edward: Don't talk about that. There is no debt between friends, which is what I hope we will be. (*He reaches to stroke her face.*)

Anne: I'll get some things together. (*Exits*)

Captain and Mathilda enter.

Captain: *(to Mathilda)* Go upstairs and stay with the lady of the house until I tell you to come down.

Mathilda exits.

Captain: Right. Plans have changed. Bumped into the King's messenger at the pub. He was clearly taking his time in getting to us but it turns out there is a spot of bother at Mottisfont. We need to get going tonight. You need to ride ahead to Romsey. Let the Abbey know we are coming and see whether the other unit has got there yet. And whether they've found that pigging Paymaster.

Edward: Hang on. Thought you wanted me to take the nun back?

Captain: Tanner can do that. You can pick up a fresh horse from your parents' farm and get there a day ahead of us. Don't gawp. You're my second-in-command and I need to get a letter from the Commander to release some funds from Romsey. I can only do that if you go ahead and buy some time.

Edward: But I've made arrangements...

Captain: Oh yes? With the missus of the house? I saw the way you looked at her. Look, I can't faff around while you make romantic assignations. Now get going. I'll follow on as soon as I get my letter.

Edward: Can I at least say goodbye?

Captain: I've given you your orders.

Edward: Can you give her a message? Tell her to hang on, to wait here until I can get back. Could be a few days. Just to wait. Please.

Captain: Yeah, yeah. Now go.

Edward: You will remember.

Captain: I'm your Captain, not your bloody go-between! Now get going!

Edward hesitates, then leaves. Mathilda enters.

Mathilda: Where is Edward?

Captain: I've sent him ahead on an urgent mission.

Mathilda: But she's just told me...

Captain: What? That Edward was going to take her away from all this?

Mathilda: What did he say? Did he say when he's coming back? She's all packed. She thought she was going today.

Captain: Well it won't be today. He'll be back in a few days. I'll give him some leave so he can come back. Just tell her to stay put. I'm going to collect the horses. Wait here and I'll send Tanner to take you back to St Mary's. (*Captain exits.*)

Mathilda: Unfeeling oaf! She's got no one. I've got my inmates at the Abbey and the Abbess is good to me and I've had my little adventure, sitting in that beer house listening to the talk of the King and the Church and what is happening in the world beyond the walls; the world of men and action, and gossip, and tough things like hunger and hard work. Makes my spiritual work look easy in comparison and I used to think it such a burden - boring. Saying prayers so often they turned to gibberish and dry leaves in my mouth. Well, my life is cushier than I knew and I thank God for it.

Anne enters with bundle of goods.

Anne: Where are they? What's happened?

Mathilda: Captain has gone to get the horses and Edward has been sent ahead.

Anne: But he was meant to take me with him. Why didn't he?

Mathilda: Look don't worry. He's going to come back. Might be a few days, though. Can you hold on?

Mathilda: I have some lentils, some rye. Enough for a few days. (*Captain enters.*)

Captain: I thank you for your hospitality, missus. Come on, you. Back to the Abbey and a life without a nice strong man to get hold of at night!

Mathilda: Please don't be disrespectful. I think I may be about to get a vocation. May God protect and keep you. (*She goes to Anne and whispers*) And he will come, I'm sure of it. (*She exits with dignity.*)

Captain: (*about to go and turns back*) Edward will come back for you. I'll grant him a few days off and he'll fetch you. OK?

Exits. Lights fade to single spot on Anne.

Anne: I know you want a happy ending. Stories my mother and father told me all had a happy ending. Bible stories had a happy ending - except when they were turned into salt or murdered each other - but this story doesn't. I waited like they'd told me to. I waited three days and he didn't come. I waited thirty three days, and he still didn't come. I waited 40 days and 40 nights until in the depth of winter, cold and with nothing to eat, I left the house. I stumbled to the tavern up the road. I beat on the door. "I hunger", I called. "I thirst", I called. They closed their ears and in the morning my body was found crouched by their unyielding door. I still wait for my Edward, for my life embraced by the green downs of Ampfield to start. And now, should a traveller be welcomed and lie down to sleep at the tavern that did not welcome me, my white arm will stretch across the centuries and twitch off the blankets. They will lie startled, the sweat of fear freezing on their bodies. And I will smile, remembering a night when a nun and captain and a sweet, sweet man came to my house and I gave them shelter.

Blackout

Rachel O'Neill has lived in Hyde for five years since escaping South London.

Hyding in Winchester

by Kath Whiting

Walking the sunshine streets of Winchester with Dog.
We slide to the side that is Hyde.
Wandering to Alfred's resting place,
But imprisoned plants and clean glass
Offer no feeling of history, no mystery.
There can be no quiet reflection here;
It is surrounded by car park.

So we flow
Up to the Hyde Gate.
Two men drug-dealering
But they are not hostile so we shake off false fear.
The gate to the gate is locked.
It says it will be open, but it is not,
Maybe the key keeper has fluttered away,
Maybe the key is lost.

I go up the steps and peer through iron bars
Dog whimpers; he knows atmospheres,
More sensitive and connected than I,
And I let him lead me away
From troubled yesterdays.

Then to the park
And through the park
And to where nuns walked.
A solitary duckling bleats and pulls my heartstrings.

This lost soul *also* pulls Dog's stomach strings,
So sadly we both away.
We follow water,
And stride out through fields.
Dog splashes happily;
A labradorian paradise.
Deer watch in statue silence.
Woodpeckering, kings fishering and more than enough
magpies.

Out to the black pipe,
Out to the dark bridge,
Derelict, drear,
Some atmospheres *are* clear.
We will go back now,
Worthiness is not for us.
Step back, step back
Through our counterfeit countryside.

A blink later and we are among allotments,
Coveting earthy treasure
Waving at our favourite scarecrows
Further in and we decide the meaning of Hyde:
(for us, for me, don't blame Dog)
The proper pub part of town.

Alfred looms large and lunchly and family full,
The Swan is the rugger lager geezer boozer,
And Hyde: the hidden treasure,
Tiny and ancient and ghosted,

With damned barstool and jars of treats,
Even a puppy to play with,
And, of course, a cellar of creativity.
Hyde, I sought and I found.

Kath Whiting lives in Upper Brook Street.

Hyde and Streak

by Christine Tulk

I am Comet, for so men have named me. I am a nucleus of nebulous light, with a luminous tail always turned away from the sun. The Greek Kometes describes my 'long-haired' tail. Composed of ice and rock, partial vapourisation, near the sun, produces my luminous, dusty, and gaseous envelope or coma. Eventually I will disintegrate to produce a meteor.

For thousands of years I have hidden myself in daytime cloud but, at night, I choose to streak across the sky. My particular chosen area of the world is called Hyde. It lies to north of Winchester, the old capital of England. From high up in space I have watched, waited and commented on the happenings below. Hence, sometimes I Hyde, sometimes I Streak. Did you not know that we comets have a sense of humour? We are a proud lot, too.

I am actually mentioned in the Annales de Wintonia. Listen to this…"In the year 1110 a comet appeared. In that year the King caused the monastery of St. Grimbald to be moved from the grounds of the bishop's church, to a suburb in the north of the city, with the monks and relics".

We comets were often seen as portents for good or evil, according to necessity. The King's palace had been extended in the centre of the town until both minsters were so cramped on one site that the organ of one deafened the other. Several times I streaked in to listen. I know little of music, but the wind singing on its way through the stars, in the soft darkness of night, is to be preferred to the sound of that instrument of earth.

Hyde meadow was rich good earth, low lying close to the flood plain, raised a little above the Winnall Moor. The flowers and bird life quailed before the arrival of men and stone. Such building, such noise, such desecration of good land, and all to the glory of God. Ah well, so be it. The Abbey at Hyde rose stout and strong. A huge gateway admitted the faithful, while the little parish church of St. Bartholomew quietly slept outside, as royalty passed by.

Two kings and a queen were buried at Hyde. Alfred, the greatest of them all, Edward, his son, and Ealhswith, Alfred's queen. Black-robed Benedictines carried on the work of God, while the skylarks still sang above what had been Hyde meadow. But during war, no birds sing. Men came with flaming torches.The night sky lit in a blood haze as the church burnt. In civil war no-one wins, least of all the poor who worked for the Abbey and depended upon it for their livelihoods.

Finally, Matilda and the Bishop Henri de Blois resolved their differences with King Stephen, and as I understand it, the Abbey was rebuilt in 1196. Time, you see, has no relevance up here in space. It flows and spins eternally, broken only by the movement of the sun and stars. People forget about us during the day, for we are not visible, but still we observe and monitor the comings and goings of our favourite patch.

After the fire, things were hard for the abbey. Bishop Woodlock raised money to complete the rebuilding, but not until over a hundred years later. By 1352 the abbey was surrendered to Bishop Edington on account of its "need, indigence and misery". The area was always poor until latter years, yet the abbey held its treasures and exacted it's payments while the people worked or starved. How else was God to be given his due? And surely the abbey healed where it could, fed where it could, and gave work to the inhabitants of that marshy place.

Yet another fire in 1445 with the bell tower and eight bells destroyed.The curfew bell still rang out from the city advising people to 'couvre feu', cover their fires till morning lest a stray spark, carried on the wind, set alight a neighbour's thatch.

Accidents happen with disastrous consequences but the whims of kings and queens have repercussions felt throughout the land. Sometime, in the middle 1500s, the tramp of feet made the ground at Hyde tremble. A peculiar sort of day, as I remember, still and with no wind, nor yet sun. I had not shown myself, or streaked. There were no heavenly portents, though rumour and fear of change were rife. A King's need for supreme power brought God's church into dissolution. The King as Defender of the Faith, but what faith cried the people? How change can destroy. And at the bottom of it all – a woman. Or so people said.

The abbey buildings, once more, fell into decay. The site was taken over, but still the townspeople arrived, quietly, to cart away a load of stone. Some, like the lead, was legitimately sold, and some lay where it fell, and the meadow flowers pushed up and covered the wounds of the severed church. When the flames died, the smoke thinned, the looting and the shouting faded away, the meadow became, once more, the children's playground. The boys fished and swam in the muddy streams. The girls picked flowers, played games and minded the little ones.

Jenna Hyde was a pretty little thing of, I suppose, four summers. Her red-gold curls, a throwback to her Viking ancestors, though no-one now remembered that, caught the sun and spun sparks of light over her gently freckled nose. Little fat baby wrists and fingers strove diligently to make a chain of daisies. Chubby knees spread on sturdy bare feet, she was the pet of all. A happy, laughing child without a care in her own secure world.

Until, one day, when she sat apart from the games and would not be cajoled into play. Even in the sun she shivered, sitting quietly, with dull eyes, while her fingers absently caressed the ring of livid spots around her upper arm. The next day she came no more. The children came and caroused as before, but not little Jenna Hyde. Not even a service in the parish church of St. Bartholomew marked her passing. Both she and the priest were part of the endless trail of carts through Black Ditch and the town, and out to the plague pits in the valley of St. Catherine. A mass grave, no intoned words to speed her passing into the beyond. Jenna Hyde was gone, and half the population of Winchester with her.

91

Not that it was all gloom and doom. Despite the plague there was some merrymaking, mischief and gossip. Jane Lambert, the mistress of Sir William Paulet, gave birth to his four sons and a daughter, while his legal wife pretended not to see, and went about her own affairs. At one time, the gracious house at Hyde held his wife, his mistress, his legal children, and by-blows. Comets are not much interested in marriage, morals or fidelity, but it seemed of great concern to the local gossips who spent more time exchanging news than working.

Hyde meadow and the abbey ruins underwent another change in 1787, and once again, the skylarks fled.They fled before the sound of men's curses as they broke the ground to build the new county Bridewell. A slow, hard business, with misery dug into the foundations, and every stone broken and lifted with a curse. A dark deed to make prisoners build their own prison. They paid scant respect to the royal bones removed from the abbey graves. Alfred, Ealhswith, and Edward the elder were tossed aside and perhaps reburied yet again, or perhaps crushed as bones and left. I cannot tell you, for I turned away, even a comet should not witness such things.

As the old saying goes, "Good Times, Bad Times, All Times, Pass Over."

And so it proved to be. In 1899 William Barrow Symonds gave the site of Hyde Abbey gate to the city. He also sold 35 acres of his water meadows, nearby, to the city for the purpose of a leisure garden. Mr. Barrow Symonds came several times to inspect the site. An imposing figure in top hat and gold watch chain. Obviously an important figure, but then, so am I. Mr. Barrow Symonds's name would go down in the history of the city, but I, if you remember, was noted in the Annales de Wintonia, at the time of my birth.

So, there was to be a beautiful green space in the middle of Hyde's crowded settlement. But first, came the planning. A competition was held in 1904 for a suitable design for the area. There was to be a cricket ground, pleasure gardens, a children's area, and other amenities. From 25 entries a winner was chosen. The prize was £75. However, the council was somewhat alarmed at his estimate of £4,500 and, in fact, the park was laid out gradually over the next few years.

Before implementing the plan, the land had to be drained. I remember hearing a Winchester man telling of how it was done.

(1) "Where the recreation ground is, that was all bog at one time. I remember when it was all bog, and all those out of work used to have to put in so many hours down there, spreading all the rubbish and stuff to make it up, so that they could get so many food vouchers."

This sounded interesting, and I streaked a little closer to listen. Of course, it was daylight so I was unlikely to be seen. People in conversation rarely look up.

(2) Another Winchester man joined in. "Where Monks Road and Nuns Road are, there was a sloping bit of water meadow and they filled it up with garbage from all the dust carts, and so on. They put houses on top of the old garbage and tins and everything. Within a few years some of the ground there sunk six foot. Eventually, they had to pull one of the end houses down, but for over twenty years the sewerage used to come over the top of the pan in four of the houses and run over into the river."

Despite the ground problems which took many years to sort out, the River Park took shape and gave people much pleasure. There were circuses and fairs, and open air concerts around the bandstand. Boating on the river was popular at 6d an hour, while the children's paddling pool was full of splashing, laughing youngsters.

William Blackman was born in 1908. Recalling his memories, I heard him say, "When I was twenty-one I had my first piano lessons. I was then singing in the Hyde Festival Choir, and Miss Lilian Brown who was the conductor offered to take me on as a pupil at half-fees".

Soon enough, the music of the choir was supplanted by the popular songs of the day, as the men of Hyde went off to war. Some returned, many did not. Despite the hardships the people of Hyde remained resolute, and community spirit was high.

After the Second World War, during which just one stray bomb fell on the corner of Hyde Street and North Walls, there were street parties, and celebrations of all kinds. The park, once more, became a park and with the advent of the 1980s came the skate park.

The youngsters spent so much time rolling up the ramps and flying down the other side. The memories of war had passed, rationing had gone and Hyde became 'posh'. The little cottages and terraced houses were full of young marrieds and families. The area began to spruce itself up as money became available and there was an air of prosperity.

The hint of a royal engagement brought the press out in force. Commander Timothy Lawrence was rumoured to be escorting Princess Anne. His week-end house at Hyde was besieged by the news people. Hyde closed ranks and protected their own. Few local people commented, and once the engagement was announced the press moved on.

Events came and went, but when the archaeologists began to open up the Hyde Abbey site, I became alert. This would have been around 1999, I suppose, and as the layers of history were peeled back it felt as thought time was slipping towards the past. It was night before I could comfortably come closer to look. The foundations lay white in the moonlight. The three pits which had once held Alfred, Ealhswith and Edward the Elder lay stark and black. The past was once more with us. What I, Comet, had once known and lost was once more revealed.

The discussions on what should become of the site seemed endless. Hard hats and clipboards proliferated, as did suggestions from the people of Hyde. Quietly, in the dark night sky, or from the shelter of a convenient cloud bank, I watched and waited.

And, oh what a triumph ensued! he site covered and raised, and the East End of the Abbey laid out, but so cleverly. Holly trees in bands of circular metal formed the pillars. The three graves chronicled by slabs each carrying a cross. The Lady Chapel beyond the high altar area marked by holly trees, this time in square metal cases, to mark the buttresses. Stone seats within the abbey space and wooden ones to indicate the side chapels.

Crowning all, an exquisite panel of clear engraving with a likeness of what was once a mighty church.

In the Autumn sunshine people sat and rested in the abbey. A man read his newspaper. An elderly lady knitted, while two others chatted in the 'side chapels'. Between the holly pillars, on a warm stone bench, a woman sat, writing. She paused to survey the scene around her. The mellow sun shone from a clear, blue sky. The holly berries glowed red within their pillar casings, while the glass panel cast dancing sparkles of light across the graves.

A young family paused to enjoy the sunshine. Three little girls, perhaps 8 years, 6 and 4 began a game while their mother subsided gratefully onto the warm stone bench.

The older girl called out the names of the three royal persons, one at a time. As she called, all three jumped onto the appropriate slab. Sometimes they jumped forwards, sometimes backwards, but often she called the same name twice and they would all jump up and down and giggle. Each one knew the name of the royal person commemorated there, and the older girl told the younger ones what had once been on the site.

Hyde's past and Hyde's future came together that afternoon, and I Comet, witnessed it all. History is all around Winchester. Come to Hyde and Seek!

Christine Tulk lives in Eastcliffe, Winchester.

My Bleak Mid-Winter Christmas Carol

by Simon Barber

Ten weeks ago, two bodies occupied this bed, and both slept. Now only one does, and does not sleep. My eyes are closed, but it's a half-hearted effort. The room lacks a woman's touch – I still have not tried to restore its old homeliness. Somehow it comforts me, as if the room suffers my loss as much as I do, sharing the burden. Not my loss; our loss. The room is not messy, just bleak. I roll under the covers onto the cold empty half of the bed, penetrating my own fort of warmth I had spent the night nurturing. It's all the motivation I need to get up.

Downstairs I sit in my dressing gown sipping absent-mindedly at a mug of sugar-less tea. The letter-knife lies discarded amongst a pile of bills. A single Christmas card towers through the mess; it is from my parents. There is a soft light spilling through the window, the first snowfall of the season apparently illuminating itself, as there is no moon to light the darkness. I decide there's nothing left for me in this house, so I throw on some warm clothes and head into the cold, shutting the door quietly behind me. My hands are thrust deep into jacket pockets, my shoulders shrugged right up almost to my ears, my breath hanging in front of my face. I meander through the Winchester back streets, my route leading past the tennis courts where once I met the girl I thought I'd spend my life with, where we played so often on summer days surrounded by crowds of cricketers or footballers or dog-walkers. Surrounded by children laughing and talking and playing with ducks in their innocent, naïve, child's world, which exists in tandem with the real world. They'll be the same kids, the same footballers, the same dog-walkers littering the white blanket in just a few hours, with Wellington-boot tread-marks and paw-prints.

But for now the snow remains flat and smooth, unadulterated, sparkling in the early light of day. The sun has not quite climbed over the horizon yet, allowing the snow to exist in shimmering peace just a little while longer before facing its bright distant destroyer. Slowly I amble towards the bench where little more than eight weeks ago I sat in the worst kind of solitude, alone in the crowd, my freshly-broken heart burning with envy for the Guy Fawkes just about discernable through the flames. Absolute solitude, which I experience now, is that little bit more bearable, as the empty world empathises. At least now there are no couples huddled together for the warmth each other provides, nor any young families, nor large groups of friends, all of which are cruel, albeit accidental, reminders of a life I once had, or could at least strive realistically for. That life I once had, those ambitions I once harboured, now lost. For now I just bask in the emphatic silence of a sleeping city, a silence disturbed only occasionally by an unreturned birdsong.

I had little concept of anything, least of all time, as I lost myself in the Arctic paradise, my thoughts entirely absent, sleeping awake, until surprised by a voice. The voice did not so much penetrate the silence as form a bubble inside it, a "Hello" spoken so softly, as if the word itself was scared to be the one to break the silence. The bubble danced and floated out of reach. Though I still had not yet seen the speaker I was immediately captivated by her soft speech, and slowly I became aware that her greeting did not mark her arrival, that in fact she had been sitting beside me for a short while. Her footsteps must have been so soft that they did not loudly compact the snow as mine did, and they barely left a print. While my track, running to our left, was clumsy and skewed, her track, running perpendicular to mine, was straight. She must have intentionally sought out either me or the bench which we now occupied together.

"Hi," I whispered, still without turning to look at her.

There was another long pause before my anonymous companion interrupted the silence again. The conversation progressed hesitantly, but was by far the biggest small talk of my life. A small breeze picked up as we talked, and while some snowflakes clung stubbornly to the branches in which they had found their home, others fell, creating a tiny blizzard between the trees which lined the river across the field. Some even fell on us from over-head branches, and she laughed as she tried to catch some on her tongue. I smiled, watching dimples appear on her soft pink cheeks, observing her care-free almost childish nature. Perhaps I was influenced by the weather that day, but I still feel now that snow suits her. I remember wondering at the time whether snowfall was positive or negative pathetic fallacy. Eventually the sun rose, we made our excuses, and reluctantly retraced footprints we had left over two hours earlier.

I took a more direct route on the way home, passing a number of children walking to St. Bede school for the last time this year, desperate to stop and play in the snow as parents hurried them along on their way. When I returned home I threw the half-mug of cold tea into the sink and put the kettle on. By the time it had boiled, the kitchen table was tidy. While my body was productive all day, my mind was engrossed in childish fantasies of our next meeting, fantasies which that night manifested themselves in dreams. It was my first significant period of healthy sleep in months. However, my slumber was interrupted by an alarm at 5.15am. This time I did not so much throw on clothes as select thoughtfully, though quickly, my outfit. Thick jogging bottoms, my warmest coat, choosing a hat was hard. Fingerless gloves, in case we were ready to hold hands yet.

By 5.35 I was out of the house, and by 5.45 I was approaching the bench again. We had not arranged this meeting, but if she was as keen as I was to cross paths again I thought the same time and place as our first encounter seemed a sensible bet. I sat for fifteen minutes, my spirits dropping significantly as more time passed. I was expected her to come across the bridge across the field, but she appeared from behind me, returning to the space on the bench she'd filled the day before.

"I thought you lived that way?" I said, pointing across the field.

"And what would you know about where I live?" she asked, a smile creeping over her lips betraying the joke in the accusation. I didn't need to tell her it wasn't meant to sound like that. The conversation flowed more freely today. I already knew about her, she'd told me that yesterday, but I didn't know her. I already knew that her name was Carol, but I didn't know she'd been named after her mother who died during the birth. I had estimated her to be no more than a couple of years younger than me, but I did not know what a bad guesser I was. I knew that she was a part-time primary school teaching assistant, but I didn't know that teaching was only ever a fall-back plan for a plan-A she never decided on. I knew she liked to sing, but I had not heard her do so. She sang 'In The Bleak Mid-Winter' as we walked in laps around the fields together, the sun rising, and my fingerless gloves proving a sensible idea. There was a combined sense of nervousness and confidence in her voice. She knew she could sing, but I think she was worried what my reaction would be. I was reluctant to let go of her hand, and would not have done so but to clap as she shied away at the end of her performance, trying to hide a sheepish smile.

The previous day's left-over snow was nothing more than slush and ice, and more than once I had to catch her as she slipped. We spent the whole day together, eating breakfast in the town, visiting the Christmas Market, walking together in the crowd; the best kind of companionship. I saw other couples holding hands, and where not long ago I would have felt an overwhelming envy, this time I felt pride. Who would not be jealous of me, walking hand-in-hand with this divine beauty, her smile white and cheeks red, a few curly locks of light-brown hair escaping from under my hat which she wore, the rest of her hair lost in the hood of her coat. We did not talk as I dwelt in new-found optimism, and I wondered if she was doing the same.

The following day we'd arranged a more sensible meeting time, and it was the first time in months I'd had a full eight hours of sleep. Once again Carol featured prominently in my dreams. We met outside the Hyde Tavern, which seemed to be a fairly central point from our houses. Though I still did not know exactly where she lived, she'd said it was just a five minute walk away. And as it was for me too, we met there at nine-thirty on that Sunday morning. She had not told me where we would be going, but I wasn't very surprised when she guided me through the doors of the Baptist Church. She smiled as members of the congregation welcomed her, including one elderly lady who beckoned us to sit with her.

"It's good to have you back, dear," she whispered, leaning in, "And who is this young chap?" she asked, though I think I was not supposed to hear.

"This is a new friend, Matthew," Carol replied.

"A good strong Christian name!" remarked the lady, whose name I later learned was Barbara. I did not comment, not wanting to seem a ill-tempered, nor give an impression of a faith I no longer had. I just smiled, and whispered a 'Hello,' and let them get back to catching up. It was the 20th day of advent, the third Sunday of Advent, and a young family lit the third advent candle. The vicar gave a talk based on a passage I knew inside-out, and yet I still made the effort to listen.

After the service Barbara invited us back to her house for a roast lamb lunch. She lived no more than two minutes away, though it took us closer to ten. Her home was small but warm, and though it seemed she did not often entertain guests it was tidy and cosy. It seemed that in one way or another all three of us were in the same place, each in need of one another. I learnt a lot about Carol in what she told Barbara. She'd just come out of a long term relationship with a boy she'd been at college with. The relationship had survived the test of distance, with him being at University in Cambridge, but his new career, it seemed, was a more important commitment. Inside, I scoffed at the idea that anything could be more important than what Carol offered. But while at some times she was an open book, at others she was closed. She dodged questions from Barbara about what she'd be doing after Christmas, and about how her father was, and I didn't wish to pry.

We spent a few more days together, but the closer we got, the more it seemed like she was trying to keep something distant. On Christmas Eve I told her I'd be at the bench in the morning, and that I'd like to watch Christmas Day dawn with her. She smiled, and said it sounded nice.

When I arrived in the morning a fresh layer of snow had fallen, and fell still. A white Christmas. I smiled. The light of the half-moon reflected on the ground and diffracted in the air. Carol was not on the bench, though a set of fresh-looking footprints led to and from the bench in the direction of her house. As I approached, I saw a square present wrapped in blue paper, speckled with white dots, and a red ribbon tied neatly around it. There was a small card attached to the bow of the ribbon, which I opened.

> *Matthew,*
> *I had to go.*
> *I'm sorry.*
> *We will meet again, soon I hope.*
>
> *xx*

I sat on the bench, her present still wrapped in my lap, and cried. By the time I left, the wrapping paper was more white than blue, with some tear-drop sized holes melted into the snow. I tried to follow her footsteps to her house, but soon they were lost under a new layer of snow.

And so was I.

Simon Barber lives in South Wonston.

Hyde Allotments

by Hugh Greasley

Wind torn flocks of pigeons
swerve over the thrashing river trees
and glow in the afternoon sun.
The peale of the bells
nails the mesh of Blackbird song
to the sunbaked shed
as a white butterfly writes
wild calligraphy over the cabbages.
Strawberried frogs dart
from my fingers into the
damp underworld

Sculpted flints
sing softly of old songs
on a dusty window sill
as honeysuckle knuckles the pane
Songs of river hunting camps,
tumbling roe buck and
feathers floating in the stream.
The roman road below
still compact from the feet
of northern tribes.
the Atrebates and the Dobunni
twists my carrots.

Anglo Saxon Wassail

by Hugh Greasley

A bird creeps into the hall
from the fox cry chill of
the never ending winter
The nervous sparrow flight
is fire flicker quick.
lancing through warm smoke
and beam shadows.
It rides the songlines
and scent of cinnamon and malt,
The fragile bird plunges through the tarry thatch
and flies out into the singing stars.

Winter Allotments

by Hugh Greasley

Radio-borne opera
trickles over the stained white walls.
Sunfall on the canyons of my sleeve
and the island of my knee
A fiery spider spins in the dark void
Outside the winterdark soil sleeps,
Crows maze the plots in soft conversation
and the vines bleed sap

Hugh Greasley is a professional artist who lives in Hyde.

A Wet Summer in Hyde

by Hugh Greasley

Temple struck by a Swallow
 in the morning barn cool
White forked flare
 and a scything swerve.
An African kiss that sings of
 Boabab roosts and
 village smoke over rusty tin roofs
 wide rivers and Hippo song.
Rain heavy
I stand lashed
In my own pool of water.

Hugh Greasley is a professional artist who lives in Hyde.

Panic in Hyde!

by Grace Romans

I awoke in pitch black and heard the sound of running feet. Then I heard my father calling with a tone of utter panic in his voice.

'Amber! The Roundheads are ransacking Winchester Cathedral! We must get the holy items out of the Church in case they want our things as we.'

I gasped. The Roundheads! My father was right. If we were going to save our holy treasures we would have to act fast. I jumped out of bed, still in my nightshirt. We both raced out of the door. It was a cool night, but even though we were on the outskirts of Winchester I could still see the dancing flames in the distance. When we reached the Church we gathered everything valuable into rough woollen bags, then me and my father, who was priest Jacob Miller, rushed to where the books for the choir were kept. I pressed the back of the ebony bookcase and slowly, very slowly, it slid back.

Then we ran, we almost flew, down the earth-smelling tunnel and the bookcase slid silently back into place. The sound of our pounding feet echoed down the passage and then back to us, its deafening sound bouncing off the walls and floor. Finally we came to a small resting room where we carefully put down our holy objects. You may have thought this room was safe, but it wasn't. It was directly under the Cathedral's nave! We sat so still it was almost like we had turned to stone. I shivered. I wished I had brought a cloak! My father spotted some thick blankets. The warmth washed through me and I snuggled into the material. Then the sound of shouting and crashing came to our ears ...

Meanwhile in the Cathedral everything was a mess. On the floor lay scattered bits of finely carved statues, a carpet of kings' and bishops' bones, beautiful bits of stained glass windows littered the floor. The Roundheads weren't gone though. They were far from gone. At the moment they were trying (and not succeeding) to destroy a lovely old statue, however their angry blows and bashes left no mark for the statue was made of bronze.

Days later we had a visitor … a messenger sent from Hyde! His name was Henry Black and he had come to reveal some relieving news. 'King Charles has returned. You can now re-place the items of the Church.'

I was so relieved. I could have done a dance I was so happy! We trudged back up the tunnel, through the sliding bookcase and, with Henry's help replaced the sacred objects. When Father and I got home I was so tired I fell asleep as soon as my head hit the pillow. I think I had quite a good sleep for I didn't remember anything until morning. When we arrived at Church for Sunday service I helped my father light 900 candles to celebrate.

Grace Romans, aged 8, is a pupil at St Bede School.

Ælfred Speaks

by Brian Evans-Jones

I used to be the core of England and the English –
'The Great', I was, and our lads shouted it
till Winchester shook. I was the rock. The hard man. The
central defender
no enemy got by; the only man to guard English turf,
English hearts.
The one to turn defence into attack
with a pin-point pass up the right or left flank
that left those Danes (the form team at the time) just
about dead.

Before I got out of the youth academy
all they had in Winchester was 'them fab'lous Roman Days'
mumbled and drooled over by toothless geezers;
but I brought the place glory.
When the champion Vejle Vikings came
to our capital – our heartland – our boys fought them on
the streets
while we drove them out
with a sound 1 – 0.
Soon those enemies feared the name of Winchester,
her crowds beating for blood.
Of course I got the call for England.
I led by example: set the dressing-room rules,
cut out the dumb feuds that had held us back before.
Taught the lads
formation, organisation, what you learn from last week's
loss.

I gave the team belief, the nation pride. And the rest,
as they say, is history.

When I died, they buried me
at the centre of my capital, in the centre of my country.
I lay and watched the pilgrims come,
their tears as they told me
how the new man, Aethel the Red, was too chicken to put
in a good tackle.
Then I heard of the bloody boardroom squabbles,
the vicious takeover by William (and let me tell you, in
Winchester,
his nickname was shorter than Conqueror.)
Those foreigners couldn't run a team like ours.
It was fine for a while: they traded on our fame,
lived off the money me and my lads had brought;
but that Norman family (Harrys, Jacks, and Dicks)
didn't trust local blood. Their fancy French wingers –
higher paid, thought they were God Himself's overlord –
buggered the team morale, made our fans
shout for the enemy.

There's only one way that can go.
Relegation. Out of the big time. The national games
gone to London. Long lipservice to my memory,
but when the developers saw a chance to make a bit of dosh
over my dead body, I got shifted as quick as you could say,
'New Cathedral Mall'.
Harry Norman Jnr. made a big show of moving me,
but where did he choose? Hyde.
(Just think about that name.)   My memory
embarrassed those new gaffers –

the anger of my loyal boys, my 'Saxons', chanting my moniker
every time the overpaid foreign softies lost 4 – 0.
And the decades on decades of obscurity,
sliding down the divisions.
Who cares about Winchester now? Who trembles at the names of Ælfred,
'Killer' Æthelwulf, Eadred 'the Shimmy'?
And since another bloody Harry had the cheek to knock my tomb down,
no-one even knows where I am.

My people tried. There's a bronze man,
fixed at the bottom of town.
It's meant to be me in full kit, showing off 'The Sword' –
winners, Northern Europe Cup, 878 –
but it ain't me. Tall, flowing-haired, noble?
My lads would laugh. 'The Great' they called me, after we won;
but in the middle of it, as I lashed at them, I was more
'That Short-Arsed, Pock-Faced, Pot-Bellied Bastard,' if they dared.

So I'm rotting in obscurity. A reserve
that no-one needs. England's defence – Winchester's strong man –
long since slipped from the changing-rooms alone.
Today's lads, kicking beer cans and each other under my bronze feet,
have no idea who I am.

Brian Evans-Jones lives in Milland Road and is a member of the Hyde Tavern Writers' Group.

Niche Market

by Lynda Horton

My terraced house in Hyde is unremarkable: blue-bagged lace curtains; a step that's scrubbed every Monday, a neat garden with borders full of rock daisies and snapdragons. On the outside I'm Mrs Average – fish on a Friday, shopping on a Wednesday and laundering on a Tuesday.

I was, I assumed, the same as everybody else in my street. My neighbours are what mother would have called a 'mixed bag'. One in particular, Mrs Jenkins, who's on the side nearest the park, is an odd one – as hard as her bobbed hair and sharp as her pointed face with horn-rimmed glasses perching on the end of a beak-like nose. She always wears old pearls about her neck - even first thing in the morning when she puts the bottles out! I only ever see her in grey or beige two-pieces that just hang off her – no meat on her ribs, mother would have said.

I don't think Mrs Jenkins has ever got over the death of her first fiancé in '43. She's gone through quite a few men since then, not that you'd think it by looking at her. (Mr Jenkins, God rest his soul, must have seen something in her.) She's always made it clear she lowered her expectations moving to Hyde.

'Do you mind, Mrs Holloway, not putting your bins where I can see them?' she says in a la-di-da accent. Or 'I wish you wouldn't park that old Anglia outside. It does so lower the tone.'

'Above her station' mother would've said, though not above (it seems by the noise on Saturday nights) lifting up her tight tweed skirt for whoever was desperate enough.

My other neighbour, Sally Jones, is on the other hand, one for a grown-up joke (one of nature's true mother figures). Cuddly, rosy-cheeked and as knowledgeable about the opposite sex as I've ever come across. She squeezes her womanly bits into figure-hugging dresses and never worries if bits bulge out. I think men love her because she's earthy.

It's Sal that encouraged me to start a guest house for men with 'unusual requirements', as she called them.

One Saturday morning she introduced me to Barry. He seemed very pleasant, dressed in normal clothes – just blue jeans and a checked shirt – nothing special for a long distance truck driver. I felt quite comfortable chatting to him, I was, however, a bit puzzled by the way Sal was watching me. When Barry disappeared from the room, she said in a loud whisper, 'So, Madge what d'yer make of 'im? Anything strange about 'im?'

'Nothing out of the usual. A bit ordinary. Why?'

'Wait and see...'

I sipped tea out of chipped china and dunked shortbread while Sal chain-smoked in between washing the pans left over from breakfast and sweeping the lino.

Our earlier conversation was completely forgotten when a lady came in to the kitchen. Seeing Sal was still busy, I offered her tea.

'Would you like a cuppa? There's one in the pot, freshly made.'

'No, Madge, I've just had one.'

'I'm sorry, have we met?'

'Er... yes Madge, not half an hour ago.'

'I'd recall you, I'm sure.'

'Madge, it's Barry,' Sal said, 'dressed as he likes to be on a weekend, away from the trucks.'

I looked from Sal to Barry with disbelief. He had put lipstick on and a blonde curly wig (which was a bit cheap looking). His dress fitted him and he had 'bits' – I can only assume they must have been socks. It's only when I looked at his enormous feet squeezed into polka dot kitten heels that it finally sunk in.

'I see, or rather I don't see. Barry, I don't understand why?'

'Please call me Bernadette. It's not something I really under-stand myself, Madge. I just need to dress up like this when I'm not working. I feel more comfortable, more sensitive. It's like being dressed as a woman, allows me to behave like one – be more in tune with my thoughts,' Bernadette half whispered, 'though I'm not a homosexual. God no! If the men found out, they'd take a brick to me or try their luck when they didn't pull. No, I love women. Perhaps that's why? Sal is the only woman I've met who understands. You still know I'm all man, don't you, Sal?'

'Hmmm, I quite sure Madge doesn't need to hear about private matters, Bernadette.'

I looked at Sal again. It was obvious from her red face that what Barry or Bernadette had hinted at was true – not that there was a 'Mr Sal' to worry about. He'd long since hopped it with a woman from the White Swan. My husband followed soon after with the pub's other 'tart-in-residence'. Where he was now, I've no idea, and I couldn't really care less. I'd struggled to make ends meet before he left, it was easier now I didn't have to feed him, pay for his drinks or pick his dirty old pants out from under the bed.

In fact, Sal's became so popular, she soon had too many guests and that's how I started my first business venture as a high-class boarding house for men with certain peccadilloes. They'd arrive on a Friday night as men, change immediately to their other self, and then change back again in time for work on a Monday morning. Some of them only lived on the other side of Winchester, but their wives wouldn't accommodate their proclivities, so they'd pack a suitcase on Friday evening, pretend they were going away on business for the weekend and book themselves into my house to act out their fantasies. We all became wonderful friends. There was Arthur/Audrey, Steven/Stephanie and Ivan/Ena.

On Saturday mornings we'd go shopping in the High Street. One of our favourites was Boots the Chemists to try the lippy, or we'd all go to the Pick 'n' Mix counter at Woollies. Stephanie always had dolly mixtures, which seemed to make the others laugh. When we'd had enough, or our feet were killing us, we'd take tea in the tearooms near the Cathedral. From there, we'd watch the world go by, flick through magazines or discuss the latest fashion and make believe we were all female friends together. I know we didn't always convince our fellow diners, the women especially were quick to see through my guests' disguises. Perhaps it's because women have an eye for detail that men don't? The gentlemen, on the other hand, were totally taken in: standing up when we came in to room, helping us with our coats and pulling seats. We got used to good manners, I can tell you. I never thought of my guests as men after a while, and it became perfectly normal to sit in my parlour doing each other's make-up or discussing how to tie a scarf to hide an Adam's apple.

On a Saturday evening, we'd get our aprons on and bake cakes. Audrey was a dab hand with the piping nozzle. She was very steady and Ena was a dream at kneading bread; she had the muscles you see, to get some air in it.

Before we served dinner, we'd run up to our rooms and get dressed. I'd normally just put a tea dress on, but the 'girls' would put on glamorous cocktail dresses with paste necklaces and feathers in their wigs. Each one wore a huge fake diamond on her finger, making believe, I suppose, that some man had wanted them enough to ask them to wed. Then we'd turn the record player on and dance to Rock 'n' Roll records. Our favourite was Bill Hailey and the Comets. I had to pretend to be the man and lead the 'girls' – we'd fling each other around, knocking ornaments off the shelves and falling over the rug.

On a Sunday morning we'd wander down the park to feed the ducks, or if the weather was really good, we'd make a picnic and all pile in to my Ford Anglia (Daphne) and drive to the countryside, where we'd picnic in a park overlooking the Downs.

Sometimes we'd have tea in the garden. Ena would dress up as waitress in a starched black dress, white frilly hairpiece and a spotless apron. She'd serve us scones and jam with our tea, which always arrived on a silver tray.

We'd only ever get half way through when Mrs Jenkins's hard heels would clickety clack down the concrete path on the other side of the fence. They'd stop for a few minutes as if she was listening and then clickety clack back up the path. She couldn't see through the fence but I know she tried. I was forever blocking up mysterious holes in the panels. We had such fun pulling faces at her from the safety of our garden.

If the weather was bad, we painted our nails and curled our lashes. It was during one such session that there was a loud knock at the door. I could see a dark figure through the glass. The 'girls' all went quiet and as I walked down the hallway I could hear kitchen chairs scraping.

I opened the door to a police officer.

'Mrs Madge Holloway?'

'Yes, constable. What can I do for you?'

'We have reason to believe that acts of indecency are being conducted on your premises.'

'I don't know where you got such an idea from, Officer! I can assure you that I keep a reputable house.'

'We have a warrant to search your house, please stand aside.'

'How dare you, Sir! You invade an innocent woman's privacy on a Sunday morning. What has made you arrive at these ridiculous allegations?'

'As I've already indicated, Mrs Holloway, we have received information.'

The officer barged his way down the corridor, two more followed him and went upstairs.

I stepped out of the door, hoping that the neighbours hadn't noticed, but I saw Mrs Jenkins watching behind the net curtains.

'It was you, was it?' I shouted loud enough for her to hear. 'What's up? Didn't manage to lift your skirt last night?' The nets twitched against the glass.

I closed the door abruptly so that it rattled the windows and went through to the kitchen. The first officer was in there making a note of what was on the table.

'I am allowed to paint me nails, am I, officer?' I waved my freshly painted nails at him. The other two policemen came in to the kitchen and shook their heads.

'Nobody else here, Sir.'

'Right.' The first policeman paused then turned to me.

'Mrs Holloway, this time we have found nothing, however, we will be keeping an eye on you. So, I suggest that you keep your boarding house in proper order. Do I make myself clear?'

'Yes, Sir. I always keep it clean and tidy. You can visit any time and find clean sheets on the beds. Do I make *myself* clear?'

He slammed his notebook shut and ushered the other two men up the corridor.

I stood for sometime in the kitchen trying to stop my hands from trembling. I didn't know where the 'girls' had gone, but they'd saved my bacon. I glanced out of the window and there, hanging on the picket fence between mine and Sal's was a pair of enormous skin pink French knickers flapping in the breeze!

Lynda Horton has lived in Northlands Drive for three years and writes prose and poetry as a hobby.

The Flood

by Matthew Bowler

Rain falling
thunder banging
river rising
water spreading
school flooding

Firemen pumping
builders fixing
painters painting
cleaners cleaning
equipment arriving

Original building
flood-proofed
modern equipment
excited teachers
children arriving.

Matthew Bowler is a pupil at St Bede School

Urban Legends of Hyde: Nick's Thumb

by Hugh Greasley

I live in a quiet Victorian suburb of a sleepy county town. It would be an idyllic life of Pimms, tennis and dog walking, if it were not for my neighbour from hell, Nick.

Nick always managed to have accidents and although he was rarely hurt or even inconvenienced by them, they usually managed to have effects you could see from space. I recalled the last bonfire night, when Nick's car sized "firework display in a box" had accidentally fallen over and rocketed the back of my house. An unfortunate strike through the cat flap had ignited an "atomic starburst" under my sink. My cat Rambo had left home following the incident and was leading a guerrilla existence in the allotments.

Events began one Sunday afternoon. Nick had inherited a Walnut tree, when he had moved next door and had subjected the tree over the years to random pruning. The tree now resembled huge hairy fist, which loomed above both our gardens. Alerted, after lunch, by the sound of a chain saw, I noticed that Nick had been carving at the base of the tree in the manner of a beaver. The tree had valiantly resisted the damage until finally with a weary creak it had swung back and forth over the gardens. It was not to be a lucky day for my greenhouse and as I ran through my garden screaming, the tree gracefully crushed the greenhouse and the orchids it contained.

This time, Nick had not been so fortunate. I found him in the garden covered by an impressive amount of haemoglobin. I had often applied term "bloody" to Nick and it was shocking to see my words become reality. In the excitement of trying to control the thrashing tree, Nick had cut off his thumb.

Later as the ambulance sirens faded, I walked down my garden, passed the flattened green house and switched off the wildly dancing chain saw. I searched for the severed thumb and even dredged Nick's pond cum moat, but the thumb was nowhere to be seen.

Two months later I was cleaning my gutters, when I found the thumb. It was dry and blackened, but looked unnaturally healthy. It almost appeared to reach out and touch my nose as I shovelled the rotting moss. The end of the thumb seemed to have a malevolent sneer. I tried to step back in horror and fell off the ladder. Later, in hospital, I had a surprise visit from Nick, who brought me some flowers. I did not have the heart to mention the thumb.

I was soon at home and limping about on my cast. Rambo the cat had returned home as part of a deal which had involved cooked chicken. Somewhere Rambo had found the thumb and had left it as "a present" at the top of the stairs. I had a fleeting glimpse of my black nemesis as I somersaulted from the top flight.

Nick again visited me in hospital and sympathised about the broken shoulder blade. He was delighted with his new prosthetic thumb, which contained a mobile phone and an MP3 player. Somewhere Nick's life long taste in heavy metal music had disappeared and his new thumb was inhabited by Madam Butterfly.

On my return home, I found the thumb sitting in a jam jar in the kitchen. It looked quite at home. A small wrinkle even gave it the semblance of a grimace and worryingly, it seemed to be growing. I took comfort that at least the thumb was now in captivity and decided to lose it for once and for all. Deep burial seemed better than cremation, because the thumb seemed indestructible. Images of the thumb crawling like "The Terminator" from my burning compost heap, flashed through my mind. I fashioned an appropriate box out of lead and placed the thumb within, along with a clove of garlic. I had thought about inviting Nick, but on reflection, imagined that he might not like to attend his own small funeral.

I remember little about cutting the unmarked high voltage electricity cable that ran under my garden. Half of Winchester missed East Enders that night, until power had been restored. Three fire engines had attended the scene.

Nick built me a summerhouse in the shelter of the crater that resulted from the explosion and I lay there throughout the summer recovering. A newspaper report noted that an historic house had burnt down because an unidentified object had jammed the fire station doors. The report had mentioned the enigmatic smell of garlic. Could the thumb have escaped the high voltage devastation?

The thumb might have ambitions, but provided it had no desire to return home, I was happy. I sat drinking tea with Nick, while Nick's new thumb-cum-ipod throbbed to the soothing sounds of Puccini.

The Time Traveller's Dream

by Alex Elms

Once there was a little boy called Alfie and he loved history. His favourite topic was ancient Hyde.

One dark windy night Alfie went to bed. He fell asleep and woke up in his dream hundreds of years ago when King Alfred was building Hyde Abbey. It looked dusty there were stones flying everywhere, it was really noisy and there were lots of people doing the building.

Noisily, a scary, scaly green fire breathing dragon with spikes down its spine and around its neck came from under the ground.

The dragon waited until night and then attached the village of Hyde. All the people in Hyde got out their armour and swords and bow and arrows; they fought back. Alfie ran to King Alfred to get some help. King Alfred came with all his best troops. They fought and fought and fought.

After a couple of days the dragon was defeated forever. All the villagers of Hyde celebrated with a big feast. Just then Alfie woke up and remembered from his dream that St Bede School was built over the top of the dragon's lair.

Everyone lived happily ever after (so far).

Alex Elms is a pupil of St Bede.

Alfred The Great

by Barry Ryan

Born 849AD in Wantage, to King Aethelwulf of Wessex
according to the many historic Codexs,
with the King's four other kids...
the youngest son being, Alfred!

Later in life, defending us from The Vikings,
who raped, stole and other wrong do-ings!
On the Northumberland's sea-shore,
then afterwards formulated a code of laws.

Alfred sought refuge, incognito ...
In a swineherd's hut, and burnt the cakes, and was told to go!
In a later date
became the King, who was very great!

Moved to Winchester, where today people are proud,
of him and probably would shout his name aloud!
Was buried in New Minister Abbey, now Hyde Abbey
as the Great Saxon, Mona-archy
in the year 899,
so please visit Winchester, to see his shrine.

Barry Ryan lives in Weeke.

Walking in a Winchester Wonderland

by Kath Whiting

Winchester is a watery place. A good place if you are an otter or a trout. You can butterfly in the Itchen or the leisure centre and later crawl to a public house. There are an abundance of hostelries in which to enjoy a fine ale and in them you will never be alone. This is because ghosts are the main customers of Winchester's inns. If you doubt me then try having a snooze in the Hyde tavern. Just don't sit on the dead man's bar stool.

There are other larger than life characters; a big pig lives at the top of town and King Alfred lives at the bottom. They may seem stony but at night they meet at the Buttercross and go to God Begot House for pizza. Yes, in Winchester there are a many meals on offer, from Hotel du Vin to the Wunderwurst Man, something to satisfy every soul.

And if it's spiritual satisfaction you're after, there are more churches per square foot than anywhere else in this world. Their scale is variable depending on the size of the parishioners. For those of small stature there is the diminutive St Swithun upon Kingsgate. Then there is the cathedral, conceived for giant folks to worship in.

There were a lot of giants before the trains came. All around town you can see relics of their residency. The Westgate is really an old croquet hoop. Tourists visit their dartboard in the Great Hall and there is a mounted toy soldier at the top of the high street. They were a playful people.

Two of the giants still live locally. Giles keeps watch over the town and has a somewhat formal Victorian approach. His sister Catherine is larger and wilder, she has an amazing tattoo and at the moment, beautiful copper hair. Recently she stopped the M3 from sheering the city in half and a little while before that she gave sanctuary to the plague dead.

The clocks used to ring out these dead. Now they compete with each other and argue all over town. They will never quite agree. The Council chimes the hour ten minutes late just to have the last word. The Town loses it at eight every evening and bongs a hundred times to assert itself. The Brook Centre is always having nervous breakdowns; it is young and unsure of itself in this community of elderly eccentrics.

The clocks' unrest is mainly due to their lamenting the lack of time there is these days. They cry down their faces and their tears fill the brooks and streams. Winchester is a watery place.

Kath Whiting lives in Upper Brook Street.

The Kitchen Floor

by David Owen Wintersgill

I realised that I was in love with you when I found myself scrubbing the kitchen floor shortly after five am one Sunday morning. There were only five hours to go until you'd arrive for your first visit to my flat and I'd woken up with the thought, 'kitchen floor', shouting in my head. This was not a thought I could recall having had before.

The previous day I had tidied and cleaned the flat. First, I'd picked a few hundred books off the carpet in order to make it visible. These were then arranged either in bookshelves or in neat stacks of eclectic combination – Tolstoy, Agatha Christie, Iain M. Banks, Ted Hughes, Nietzsche. Once the carpet was clear, I began dusting. Dusting, incidentally, is best done to punk music – it has the right level of energy and pogoing helps get you up into the high corners. So I bounced about the room to Stiff Little Fingers and only broke one rather hideous vase which had been donated to me by an aunt of high morals. After a thoroughly deserved visit the pub to refresh and fortify myself, I returned to begin hoovering. It is a sad fact but hoovers have no taste; they are indiscriminate and soulless – pausing only occasionally to register disgruntlement with pieces of loose change. Thankfully, I was soon able to turn to washing up accompanied by some of Grieg's piano music. Fairy liquid and Nordic fjiords – a hard combination to beat.

After that, it was just a matter of a quick run to the Tarbuck's corner shop to pick up the food and a more lingering visit to Bottoms Up, the off-license. I was now thoroughly prepared – which meant that I could spend the evening in the pub not least because I was, I think, morally obliged to eat there in order to preserve the pristine state of the flat. One or two – ish – drinks later I returned and retired. But then I woke up at 5am with the thought, 'kitchen floor', pounding in my head.

It was an unfortunate truth that the kitchen floor had lain undisturbed by cleaning products for about two years, ever since Rita, the mad Glaswegian cleaning lady who juggled wine glasses and lifted the heads of sleeping guests off the futon in order to dust under them, had inexplicably chosen to leave. And its surface was, I admit, a little sticky – perhaps not enough to pull a sock entirely off one's foot but enough to draw it down a little.

So I hauled myself out of bed, dug deep into the cupboard under the sink – found a lost copy of Aesop's Fables – and got out various bottles of bleach, white powder and creamy stuff. I poured, shook and squeezed some of each of these into the washing up bowl, added water, and armed with a small square sponge lay down on the floor to clean it. I say 'lay down on the floor' because that's what I did; it was not an altogether ideal move given the stickiness to be addressed, but my amusing combination of patella tendonitis and arthritis in both knees meant that kneeling was acutely painful if indulged for more than a very brief period, so instead I lay on my stomach and engaged in a kind of breaststroke up and down the kitchen floor. Later, through sheer boredom, I switched to lying on a hip as if in a horizontal side-saddle and slither-trotted up and down. Eventually, it seemed clear that the floor was clean – it had stopped being obviously sticky. So I had a shower and went back to bed.

A year later, on the day we moved into our house in Hyde, the week before the wedding, we sat among boxes eating paper-wrapped fish and chips and drinking champagne. You recalled how touched you'd been at all the trouble I'd taken that Sunday, the obvious effort I'd made to clean and tidy. Then you paused – we weren't yet married - and said that you guessed it was a male thing, perhaps a genetically encoded blindness, but you remembered thinking on that first visit that it was only a pity that it hadn't occurred to me to clean the kitchen floor.

David Owen Wintersgill lives with his wife (and now children) in Hyde.

The Gate-Keeper's Story

by Faith Clarke

'Hey, you,' said Gary, 'You know you shouldn't climb on this gate. GET OFF. GET OFF right now!'

'Oh,' sighed Gary the gate-keeper, ' five years of gate-keeping and still those boys won't stop climbing on my gate. I've got to guard this gate as I have been told so many times. Oh, look at the time. Almost time to lock up for the night.'

Just as Gary was locking up something very peculiar happened. Out of nowhere appeared an oddly dressed man with a long white beard and long black robes with stars and crescent moons on. Gary stared at him in amazement.

'I am Wizard Whitebeard and I am 5950 years old and I am here to give you this.' The wizard handed Gary an old tatty looking diary.

'The Diary of Hyde Gate,' Gary read. 'Hyde Gate? Hyde Gate? Well, that's the gate I guard and what I'm guarding right now,' said Gary, looking startled. ' But how? What? Where? What am I meant to do with this diary?' asked Gary, a little puzzled.

'Well,' said the wizard, 'you could open up a page and you will instantly be taken to whatever special time in the history of Hyde Gate is on that page.'

In a flash the wizard disappeared into thin air. Gary, still a little puzzled, looked at   the diary and thought to himself, 'I wonder if I should open a page now or later?'   Without thinking any more, he closed his eyes and opened a page in the book. When he opened his eyes Gary found himself in front of a gate. He wondered where he had seen it before. Gary nervously walked forward until he felt a heavy push on his chest. It was a hand.

'Are you someone who thinks he can burn Winchester?'

'N... n...n...no.'

'What are you wearing? Are you from somewhere else?'

'Yes,' said Gary.

'Then come with me,' said the man pulling Gary's coat sleeve very hard indeed.

An hour later they arrived at what seemed to be a palace or a sort of castle. The two men walked in. Soon they came to a door with a sign on it that said COURT ROOM.

'A... a. . . are we going in there?' said Gary, filled with terror.

'Yes,' said the man, coldly. They walked in slowly. 'Sit down,' said the man. Gary sat.

Suddenly some people came in and sat down then out of a door at the back came four more people. One sat at the front, one sat on the left, and another sat on the right. The last one sat on a chair in the middle.

'David,' said the man in the middle chair and the man who had caught Gary stood up.

'This man is planning to destroy Winchester,' said David and everyone gasped. 'He's got plans in the book in his hand.' David snatched Gary's diary and gave it to the judge in the middle seat.

'NO!' screamed Gary as he jumped up and caught the diary.

Without thinking where he would go, without even knowing if he would make it back, he closed his eyes and opened a page in the dairy. When he opened his eyes again he saw the most amazing sight.

'Uh – ho – here we go again!'

Faith Clarke is a pupil at St Bede School.

Going Back to Hyde

by Karen Marsh

'As I count down from five to one...relaxing more and more,' the therapist's voice trailed off into my subconscious.

I felt the leather of the chair clawing at my limbs and dragging the tension away.

'Now look down at your feet, what shoes are you wearing? Where are you?'

I lowered my head and stared at the blackened nails edging the disfigured feet beneath me. The left foot moved forward and I winced at the pain as it lowered back onto the path. Each carefully considered step incurred another ecstasy of pain, contrasting with the serenity around me. My emotionless face never alluded to the cries of joy that were ringing inside my head. A double-edged feast of sensations meant I was at last feeling something; anything.

I studied the hollow eyes of the faces around me, duty bound, chastened or at least they appeared to be. I wondered if the oppressive flint walls were sucking the life out of all within, or whether the claustrophobia was endured only by the impostors like me. I should belong here, we shared a uniform, a prayer, a meal; but my jaw was tense and restrained, the words of many obedient years gridlocked in my throat.

'What about your clothing, who is with you? Remember you can talk,' the therapist interrupted.

'I'm in my robes, working the ground. To labour is to pray, the words keep ringing round my head. But I don't know why I've come here, I didn't want this life,' my voice broke through with a parched whisper.

I look around at the other brothers tending the field, fearful that they had heard me.

As I ease my back upright, I pace slowly and heavily towards the flint wall. I savour each step, purposefully forcing one foot after another against the jagged surface of the ground. My breathing has become laboured and noisy as I drag the air in through each nostril. I fall back against the wall for support and slide down into a sitting position. The rough edges of the flint slicing pathways down my back, but I am oblivious now.

I lift my hooded eyes to see the brothers moving towards me, concerned looks finally bringing life to their faces. But it's too late I have only one way out of this.

'I have sinned, I have sinned,' I try to cry out to the therapist, but no sound comes from my moving mouth.

Instead, the brothers, startled by the loud female voice, had stopped wide-eyed, a few paces in front of me. They drop to their knees, reaching out in prayer.

'Bless our brother, for he is possessed,' they chanted fearfully, over and over, as the noise begins to overwhelm me. Their faces merge and the voices drift into the distance as I feel myself lifting up and out in joyous freedom. My soul turns to look back at the scene, as my awareness rests down next to the stream.

The brothers pray over the empty body for several hours before carrying it to its final resting place, and burying it deeply along with the secrets of its possession.

The hypnotherapist counted me back from the trance and left me pondering the authenticity of my past life regression.

A walk by the stream and flint walls at Hyde gate, sometime later did little to dispel the mystery. As I bent down, I found my hand tracing the pattern of deeply stained jagged stones running down to the ground in front of me; a bloodstain that could have been engrained for 900 years.

Karen Marsh lives in Winchester and comes to the Hyde900 'Bring-Your-Own-Literature' events at the Hyde Tavern.

The Friends' Secret

by Emelia Jarvis

One day Amy Kennedy asked her Mum if she could meet her friends and go to Hyde Abbey Church remains. Amy had been learning about it at school, and she wanted to have a look. Soon she found her friends, Lilly Stevens and Jess Jones, and they ran off towards the remains.

When they got there, Amy went off and suddenly she shouted, 'Hey guys, come and look.'

Lilly and Jess came running after her. When they got to her, Amy said, 'Help me move this big stone.' And underneath it there was a flight of steps going down into complete darkness. Amy went down and Lilly and Jess followed closely behind. At the bottom of the steps was a strange machine.

'Look – a space rocket,' shouted Jess.

'I don't think it's a space rocket, Jess, I think it's a time machine,' cried Amy.

'Oh,' said Jess, sounding very shocked.

Without thinking, they got in the time machine and Jess pressed a button quickly. Soon everything was changing swiftly around them. Then it stopped and Lilly got out, running across the field, and standing in front of her was a huge abbey.

Lilly rushed inside and Jess and Amy ran in after her. They found her staring at the wonderful stained glass windows. As they were trying to work out what was on the window, it smashed. The girls ran behind a cupboard and Amy looked over the top. She saw King Henry V111 and all his knights on horses jump through the window. They were searching for treasure.

Suddenly Henry shouted, 'Burn the whole building down.'

Amy screamed, 'Run!'

They ran through the hall, back to the tomb where the time machine was. A knight had spotted them and he was chasing them down the steps. He was just about to grab them when they jumped into the machine and pressed the button.

When they were back at home it was very late. They had been away for two hours. Just then Amy fell over and she felt a funny cold feeling in her jumper.

It was a ruby. It was beautiful and that is her very special secret she has to this day.

Emelia Jarvis goes to St Bede School.

Nuns Walk (the start of a play...)

by Michael Craze

ACT 1 SCENE 1 WINCHESTER 1110AD

NARRATOR: Lord God, creator of heaven and earth and the universe, please forgive us our sins. Especially those we commit in your name.

Bells ringing as camera pans out from the gargoyle of a monk on the cathedral. Gregorian chanting as we see a low winter sun reflecting off the gold cross of King Cnut being carried by a monk next to the Abbott at the head of the procession followed by the remains of Alfred the Great, his wife Ealswith and their son Edward the Elder. They move with stately solemnity through the ancient capital and then through fields to the main gate of the new monastery, past the church of St. Bartholomew's and down the hill to enter the monastery church. The great wooden doors are closed and we then cross fade 30yrs to 1140AD and the doors of the Scriptorium being opened to reveal a young novice, (Barnabas) carrying vellum, being ushered in tersely by one of the artist monks (Robert). We see scenes of the illumination of books etc. (e.g. The preparation of the various inks and dyes used. The bells then ring to herald the start of one of the many services of the day. General hustle and bustle on the way to the church. The main gates of Hyde Arch are opened as monks, nuns and local peasants return with farm produce from Abbotts Barton (The Home Farm). They are off loading bails of barley when one of the nuns loses her footing in the muddy courtyard and tumbles into the pathway of a group of novices led by Barnabas. The brothers cascade over the hapless nun and a general "slaphazard" scene ensues. This is abruptly ended by the arrival of the Abbot and his entourage. His presence and admonishing look are more than enough to curtail the commotion. He proceeds to the church leaving the elders of the brethren to muster the bespattered novices into some order. The nun accepts a helping hand proffered by Barnabas and as she regains her feet she turns to face him. We see, even through the mud, that she is mortifyingly beautiful. She is embarrassed by the disturbance she has caused and also by the obvious attention paid to her by Barnabas.

NUN: Brother.

MONK: Sister.

They are both hurried along to the service. Inside the church there are moments of eye contact between them (overseen by Brother Robert). The service ends and the Nuns leave to return to the Nunnaminster of St.Mary's, in the city of Winchester. The nun looks back to catch the eye of the monk. They smile. The Hyde Arch gates are closed. That night we see them both in prayer in their separate cells (Rosaries), cross fading voices in tandem. But once they have retired they recall the incident in the courtyard and echo their earlier smiles.

ACT 1 SCENE 2 - MORNING FISHING

It is morning and we see the breath of the monks in the cold air as Barnabas and Robert struggle with a crudely built fishing boat. They carry it to the water's edge and set themselves afloat. General scenes of early fishing and Hampshire countryside. They settle in their task. The mood is convivial.

ROBERT: The good Lord forgive me, Barnabas, but a morning spent fishing, inspired by all the natural senses will settle the mind to an understanding and peace unrivalled in a lifetime of contemplative prayer and meditation. (Beat-sign of the cross).

BARNABAS: The good lord I am sure will forgive you Brother Robert. There is a real peace in this place. Even the cold feels different. More correct. Just as cutting in the cloth, but more correct.

ROBERT: When left alone unspoilt within its own order nature is correct. Calm and content.

BARNABAS: Calm and content.

ROBERT: Yes Barnabas. It is something none of us can fully appreciate until it is taken from us. Not just the peace of physical security, warmth and brotherhood, but more importantly, peace of mind. The inner tranquillity.

BARNABAS: It is a glorious morning.

ROBERT: Remember this place. Visit here often and learn from the stillness. Carry the soft sunshine of this day with you and use it as a silken cloth to bandage your soul and strengthen your spirit.

BARNABAS: We have our faith Brother.

ROBERT: We have our faith. But the good Lord knows there are maladies that can pull the mind from its axis leaving it frightened,

133

bitter, angry and even faithless. But, if we contain within ourselves the natural order and inner peace felt on such a day as this, then we may find our way back to sanctuary. To know that somewhere in the world there is peace is to know that not all is submerged in a deranged darkness and that it will right itself again. It is natures' way.

BARNABAS: Correct, calm, content. There is no deranged darkness here Brother Robert.

ROBERT: No. But will it come, Barnabas, if King Stephen and Empress Maud have their way. (beat) Anyway, enough food for the soul. We must feed our bellies. (ABBEY BELLS) Oh, and those of our good Brethren too. (Laughter in their work as we fade.)

Michael Craze has been local to Hyde for 44 years. His mother's family arrived from Lymington in 1939 to run the Eagle Hotel. He is a Winchester City Tour Guide.

Faulty Goods

by Neil Dewey

Not so long ago, one day in late August last year actually, I saw someone opening their car boot in Arthur Road and the sky fell out.

Not all of it – just a huge cloud that must have been deliberately squashed in. The car was a Fiesta or something similar. Silver, I think. Nothing out of the ordinary. If I remember correctly, the man was wearing jeans and a forgettable tee-shirt.

The cloud though, I do recall. It was an evil grey, with hints of angry black. Looked like an anvil with lots of ziggy zaggy flashes of lightening within it. But sort of pent up, because none came out and you didn't feel the need to start counting seconds off just to see how far away it was, and how long before the thunder.

And having fallen out, the cloud just hung around, uncertain, like a caged animal faced with the novelty of an open and unattended door – as if it was considering the sniff of freedom but at the same time being troubled by a concept pretty much forgotten.

To tell the truth, it was a bit of a shock. Something outside of my experience. I'd have liked someone, anyone, a total stranger, an impartial to confirm my observations. But apart from us; me, the man, and his cloud, the utterly normal street was empty.

The man didn't appear to be surprised.

How did I know it was his cloud? Well, obviously I couldn't be certain, but apart from it being the only way the scene made any sense to me, it was how he spoke to it. Frankly, he was thoroughly uncomplimentary. I couldn't hear everything, but it was his tone and something about, 'You've had forty days, I've fed you, and all you've done is fizz and crackle,' that suggested he was not a happy man.

I should have asked him casually, as you do in North Walls Park for instance, 'That your cloud? Nice. What's he called? Don't see too many Nimbo-cumuli around here!'

And he'd say something like, 'No. They're tricky. Unstable characters, if you don't train them right.'

Then you'd pass on by.

But he was too far away, it wasn't the park, and it seemed rude to shout from where I stood.

So I watched as the man took a food store bag from the back seat. He unfolded it carefully: gave it a good shake so that the sides were not stuck together. From my position, it looked to be one of those environmentally correct re-usable ones – the thick plastic type with all that marketing hype about how long they've been around... you know the sort of thing.

Anyway, he stuffed the cloud inside like it was a pile of tangled dirty knickers ready for the launderette. You could see the electric blue zigs and zags through the printed polythene, concentrated like seedy disco lights that embarrass you and your dandruff.

Then, the weirdest thing. He kind of put his arms round a big lump of air, as if he was picking up a Swiss exercise ball round its middle, and pushed that in too.

When he did that, the late summer street smell became heavily tinged with seaside and seaweed. The sort of must-take-a-lungful-of-this-it's-bound-to-be-healthy-aroma that entices you to get stuck in traffic jams in July. Except that hard as I tried to breath, the process seemed to go into reverse. I felt faint, and more than a little breathless until I moved back down the road.

It didn't seem right – it still doesn't – stealing lumps of air and chunks of sky, but by then I was too far away to raise the point with him.

I've spent the last few days wondering exactly what he did with the shopping bag – and its contents. Really, I should have taken a chance on the atmosphere. It was probably all in the mind. After all, the man didn't appear to be having any breathing problems. I could have gone back and asked what he was up to.

There again, I'm probably making a big deal over nothing. Because the last I saw of him, he was heading towards the centre of Winchester – with his flashing food bag. I like to think he was going back to the store the cloud and bag came from. They're quite fair, I'm told, with their exchange and faulty goods policy. Well, with most things. Normally.

Neil Dewey hopes to move to Hyde when he sells his house, in the meantime he enjoys the Hyde Tavern.

iShades

by Andy Key

Aaron looked in the living room mirror. A balding, middle-aged man stared back, the remaining hair greying round the edges. Around his eyes, the flesh sagged and the beginnings of a double chin were visible beneath the thin mouth.

Aaron sighed and reached for his glasses case. Opening it, he unfolded the arms of his iShades and put them on, pushing the frame up onto the bridge of his nose and hooking the arms snugly over his ears. Tiny earphones swung down to nestle in his ears.

For a moment, random colours flashed in front of his eyes, then the words 'Starting up... Welcome to iShades.' Abruptly his vision cleared. He glanced in the mirror again, seeing a trim young man with thick dark hair and a firm jaw, wearing a stylish pair of sunglasses. He smiled, and the image smiled back, displaying a row of perfect, glacier-white teeth.

Aaron picked up the bag full of bottles and headed for the door. 'Jen, I'm just going to the recycling,' he shouted up the stairs. His wife appeared at the top, clad in a croptop and shorts, her tanned body filling the clothes in all the right places. On her face she wore her own iShades – last year's model, slightly heavier than Aaron's brand new pair. For a moment he felt the urge to push his own iShades up and see her for real, but these days they both preferred to avoid doing that.

Aaron walked down to the park. As he passed through the gate, a noticeboard appeared, floating in mid-air over the path, reminding him of the park byelaws. A voice in his right ear started reciting a litany of safety warnings. With a slight nod he acknowledged the warnings, and both sign and voice vanished.

By the leisure centre, Aaron tipped bottles into the recycling bank. Bright-coloured animated banners clamoured at the edges of his vision, advertising special offers on fitness classes and swimming sessions. He blinked them away.

Aaron glanced up at the late autumn sunshine, which conveniently dimmed as his iShades tracked his eye movement. It's a nice day, he thought. I'll go for a stroll.

He glanced through the windows of the gym as he passed. Four men sat in rowing machines arranged end to end, heaving at their imaginary oars in perfect time. A floating label popped into view, attaching itself to the lead rower. *Winchester City Rowers, Second Coxless Four*, it informed him. The voice in his ear added, 'League race against Adelaide.'

'Show race,' commanded Aaron, and the blank walls of the gym faded away. The rowers were seated in a real boat, and beyond them he could see the Adelaide boat, caught in a ptch of choppy water and trailing badly despite the frantic efforts of its crew. Beyond them he could see the banks of the Torrens River, the occasional black swan drifting past on the muddy waters, and beyond it the bustle of central Adelaide.

He watched the Winchester team cross the finish line, applauded politely, then dismissed the image and continued his walk, past the playground and on round the edge of the park.

Aaron crossed the rugby pitches and stepped onto the wooden bridge that led over one of the many streams into the wildlife reserve.

As he did so, he spoke out loud: 'Enable WildSpotter app: add Wiki and English Nature databases.'

'App enabled,' the iShades' voice replied smoothly. 'Scanning for wildlife.' A flurry in the reeds downstream caught Aaron's attention. He turned and his iShades zoomed in on the disturbance. A large white bird burst forth, flapping its wings slowly as it heaved into the air. A label popped up and chased it across the sky, reading *Little Egret (Egretta Garzetta)*. The voice spoke in his ear. 'Little Egret. Breeding pairs common across southern England; rare elsewhere in Britain.'

Aaron turned left and headed along the path into the depths of the reserve, taking him away from the park and the city and into the water meadows to the north. As a walked, the iShades tagged various plants and wildlife – a blackberry bush here, a water vole there, three varieties of duck and, once, a distant flash in the far field which it confidently identified in its smooth tones as a roe deer.

Aaron reached the furthest point of the path and turned to go back. Suddenly, about twenty yards back the way he'd come, there was a heavy rustling in the bushes near the path. A tag popped up. *Possible mammal: insufficient pattern data to match. Suggest closer inspection.* Aaron zoomed in on the spot but nothing was visible. He started back towards the area.

The bushes moved again and something like a large, shaggy dog stepped out onto the track. A label flickered over its head, but remained blank. After a few seconds it flickered out again. 'Identify the animal,' Aaron commanded. The label reappeared but remained stubbornly blank. The animal stared at Aaron, its jaws slightly parted, the corner of its tongue lolling out. Aaron stared back, motionless.

Finally, the label reappeared. 'Positive identification,' murmured the voice in his ear.

Aaron stared aghast at the words in the label: *Grey Wolf (canis lupus)*

'Extinct in England since the sixteenth century,' the iShades' voice added, helpfully.

'Generally timid around human beings. Identification 91% confidence level.'

'It doesn't look bloody timid to me,' muttered Aaron.

Perhaps hearing his voice, the wolf's ears pricked up. Its lips curled up and back, revealing long white teeth.

The iShades' voice chipped in again. 'Erect ears and displayed incisors are usually a sign of anger.' After a pause, it continued, 'Social behaviour: Occasionally, single wolves are found in the wild, however packs are more common.'

Slowly, reluctantly, Aaron pulled his gaze away from the jaws and looked to his right. There, a few yards to the right, was another wolf, slightly smaller than the first but no less terrifying. And then another stepped into view to his left. And another. The iShades tagged each one as it appeared, and the voice announced, 'Probable family group.'

'Call 999,' said Aaron quietly, standing as still as he could. Near the bottom of his vision the word *Connecting...* appeared. He watched the progress bar as it grew slowly from left to right... and then stopped. *No Connection.*

'What?' he hissed. I'm in the middle of Hampshire, how can there be no connection?'

'Regrettably no uplink is currently available, said the voice, 'Downlink data stream only. You may wish to consider adding a secondary service provider to your contract. Please note, however, that 24 hours' notice is required for contract changes.'

'Uh... Help?' Aaron half-shouted, half-whispered. There was silence. He was at the far end of the nature reserve, well away from the park. Around him were streams, open meadows and clumps of undergrowth and trees. He realised that he hadn't seen another human being since he left the leisure centre.

The lead wolf made a low growling noise and crouched back slightly. 'Crouching posture typically indicates an intention to attack,' Aaron's iShades informed him.

Aaron's trance broke. He turned and ran. He reached the end of the path and kept on running, floundering through a patch of tall nettles and on through high rushes. He hit a head-high mesh of briars and tripped head-first into them, clawing himself upright again and scrambling over them on his front, his clothes catching and tearing. He fell head-first on the other side, staggered upright and ran again, not daring to look back. In his ears he thought he could hear the sound of panting, not far behind. He knew he was being forced away from town, further into the countryside, but there wasn't much he could do about that. He ploughed across an open meadow of long grass and into a copse, following a faint animal track into the depths of the wood. Darting behind a large tree trunk, he peered back out to the meadow.

For a moment he thought the wolves had gone, but then the iShades started popping up pointers one by one, floating above the field, each meticulously labelled with estimates of size, weight and age. Following the pointers, Aaron could see the ears and shaggy dark backs moving through the undergrowth. He turned to run again and immediately tripped over an unnoticed root, falling sideways and whacking the back of his head on the adjacent tree. He fought off the dizziness and ran on through the wood. Within seconds he was brought to an abrupt halt as his forehead collided with a low branch. He toppled backwards and swore loudly. Where the hell did that come from? It was dull in the wood, but not dark, and the iShades had turned up the gain automatically so he should have seen anything in his path. He staggered on, weaving slightly. His vision blurred and the ground seemed to tip and buck in front of his eyes.

Out in the open again, Aaron looked back. The wolves were closing on him, their tongues lolling as they cantered steadily, inexorably closer. He turned and ran on toward a river a few yards ahead, promptly colliding with a barbed-wire fence which ripped a gash in his right thigh and pierced his hands as he instinctively grabbed at the wire to break his fall. He wrestled the wire from his leg, making the cut longer and deeper, and toppled over the fence. On hands and knees, the sound of the wolves breaking through the rushing noise in his head, he half-crawled to the river's edge and threw himself in. The cold knocked his breath away and penetrated his limbs, making them feel heavy and sluggish. The current grabbed him and pulled him towards the deep water in the middle of the stream, sweeping him quickly downriver. Feebly treading water, Aaron pulled his iShades from his face and wiped a trickle of blood from his nose. He looked back at the bank, but the wolves were nowhere to be seen. Where were they? Had they followed him into the water? He replaced the iShades. Ah, there they were – the zoom function picked them out for him, running parallel to the bank, tracking him down river. He struck out away from them towards the far bank, his clothes dragging in the water.

As he neared the far side, the current changed and he found himself being swept diagonally towards the bank. Faster and faster it went, closer and closer until, just too late, he realised why. The water slammed his body up against the metal grating of a weir, pinning him against it, tangled in a mass of debris and rotting weeds. He tried to grab at the riverbank, but it was curved and slippery and his hands didn't seem to have any feeling. He swam away, against the flow, and for a moment broke free of the grating – but then the world seemed to spin round him and before he knew it he was jammed against the grating again.

He tried to cry out, but water bubbled into his mouth and down his throat, making him cough and retch. His right leg wouldn't move – it seemed to be caught in a cluster of weeds on the riverbed. The sky span again and his head went under. He turned round and grabbed at the railings and peered up at the bank above him. A shadow fell across his sight.

'Grey Wolf,' the iShades informed him, the voice now slightly crackly as if the water had got into the earphones. 'Male, estimated weight 60 kilos.' The wolf's head lunged down at him and he ducked beneath the water. He held his breath as long as he could before bursting up, gasping. Immediately the great jaws snapped above him and he ducked again. Five times this happened – or was it six? He could no longer think straight enough to count. On the seventh ducking his iShades came off and were swept through the gaps in the railings. He emerged above water to find that the wolf had gone, perhaps tired of the game.

Aaron knew he should try to escape now, but somehow it didn't seem worth the effort. The cold that had been so paralysing at first now seemed to have worn off, and maybe if he just waited here a while he could – could – something. Anyway, he… needed to… call home. That was it. But his iShades had gone somewhere, so it would have to wait. And anyway, he needed to call home, and… no, that wasn't it. Maybe he'd just rest for a minute. That would give him strength to get out.

Aaron lay back against the rushing waters. A swirl of red flowed away from his body and into the weir.

***

The sergeant sat next to Jen on the sofa.

'Just a couple more things, Mrs Whittaker – was your partner a habitual user of any narcotic drugs? I'm sorry, but we have to ask these questions.'

Jen shook her head, not trusting herself to speak in case she burst into tears again.

'Was he depressed at all? Problems at work, maybe?'

Another shake.

'I'm obliged to inform you that I have recorded this interview on my iShades.' The sergeant tapped the arm of her own eyewear. 'Do you have any objection to me archiving it as evidence?' Another twitch of the head. 'Thank you. It's important that we have a reliable record.'

The sergeant nodded to the bereavement counsellor, quietly left the house and walked down the street to her car. Leaning on the vehicle and looking at the trees, she instructed her iShades to call the inspector. After a moment, his face appeared, floating disembodied in front of her.

'Not much to report, sir. Still no explanation for his behaviour. From the injuries he received before immersion, it looks as if he was running away from someone, but there's no evidence of anyone else having been in the reserve at the time. We've found his iShades about half a mile downstream and the memory was intact, but he seems to have switched off the logging functions as he left the park. Yes sir, I know, the third one in six months. No sir, no idea. Yes, I'll let you know straight away.'

144

The inspector's image faded. The sergeant glanced once more towards the meadows beyond the park. As she went to open the car door, a distant movement caught her eye...

Andy lives in Nuns Road. He grew up on Teg Down Meads, but refuses to apologise for it. He wrote this piece for a science-fiction-themed evening at the Hyde Tavern.

The Hyde Cat

by Sonny Matthews

The Hyde Cat,
The Hyde Cat,
Is an alley cat.
He sleeps by day and he steals at night,
O that sly Hyde Cat,
O that sly Hyde Cat.

All that you can see at night
Is that black cat's green glowing eyes.
O that sly black Hyde Cat,
O that sly black Hyde Cat.

The Hyde Cat is busy at night
But asleep by day,
O that sly black busy Hyde Cat,
O that sly black busy Hyde Cat.

The Hyde Cat cannot be seen by night
Because he's camouflaged.
O that sly black busy camouflaged Hyde Cat,
O that sly black busy camouflaged Hyde Cat.

The Hyde Cat is as cunning as a magpie
And as hidden as a secret.
O that sly black busy camouflaged cunning Hyde Cat,
O that sly black busy camouflaged cunning Hyde Cat.

Sonny Matthews lives in Worthy Road and goes to St Bede School.

My House In King Alfred Terrace

by Ralph Roseppy

Where my house is in King Alfred Terrace, is the site of the old Hyde Abbey hospital which was used by the monks in the old days. A horrible murder happened in the hospital in these times. A person who was a member of King Henry V111's parliament was murdered by one of the friars (not a fish fryer) who lived at the Abbey, and the murdered person's family wanted revenge. The family wanted to pay them back for the murder for many years.

Then one night in the 1980's the family took their revenge by setting fire to the River Park Leisure Centre, that had been built near where the Abbey hospital used to be. This made the murdered person's family very happy, as they thought they had got their own back on the evil friar. Luckily though, the fire was put out and the Leisure Centre damage was fixed, which is good as I can still do my football there!

Ralph Roseppy is in Wykeham class in St Bede School.

Hyde and Seek

by Emily Maynard

Once there was a boy called Tom and a girl called Emily. One day Emily was digging in the St Bedes school garden when she came across an old and slightly mouldy book. She gave it a good wipe and saw it said 'DIARY 1848' on the cover. How odd! she thought, 'I'll have a quick read,' she said out loud to herself and Emily opened the diary to the first page:

> *My name is John Day-Brown. I am ten years old. My mother and father are dead. They left me some money in their will so I could learn to read and write but now I live with horrid old grump face, Lord Norris. I am so fearful of him. He even tried to kill me once. Luckily the maid came along and asked him what he was found. He just said that his new sword needed a polish and then he walked off quickly.*

Wow, this is amazing; I'll have to tell Tom, thought Emily. So later that day Emily told Tom all about it and showed him the diary up until where she'd read.

'Wow,' said Tom. 'You must read more.'

'Oh yes,' said Emily, and she turned over the old page carefully to see that some of the next pages were missing. 'Oh,' said Emily, 'most of the pages have been ripped out.'

'Maybe he didn't need them,' replied Tom, 'just go on to the next page there is in the diary.'

> *I live in Hyde House and I saw Lord Norris, my guardian, holding a Golden Sceptre. He must have stolen it. I pray he didn't see me... Oh no, he did ...*

Emily read out loud in a worried voice.

> *I am hiding in the Monastery at Abbey Gate. I can hear heavy footsteps. It must be him. These may be my last words... Please, if you can find the Golden Sceptre, Lord Norris must be punished.*

'Oh gosh, all that's on the last page is blood and ink,' said Emily.

'Wait a second. Where did he say he dies?' replied Tom.

'The monastery,' they both said at the same time. 'Why don't we check it out and see if there are any clues to show us where the Sceptre could be hidden.'

After school finished, Tom and Emily walked to Hyde Abbey gate. They found nothing and were very disappointed. They decided to have a very careful look just in case they had missed anything. 'Tom, Tom, I've found a hole. Come over and have a look.'

Just to the left of the door on the old stone wall, covered in cobwebs and hidden by moss was something peeping out. 'It's some paper,' said Emily, carefully taking out the old paper. 'It's the missing pages, Tom.'

'Pass them here,' said Tom, 'wait, one piece is bigger than the others,' he said. 'Read it, Emily.'

Whoever finds this, I am probably dead now, but the Golden Sceptre is in the place where the diary was found.

'And?' asked Tom.

'And what?'

'What else does it say on the paper?'

'Nothing.'

'Well let's go and get that Sceptre - or should we read the diary first?'

'Yes, but let's hurry back to school at the same time before the gates shut.'

It's night now and I have moved under the bridge by Hyde Monastery. My feet are wet and it is cold but I have nowhere else to go. I think I will have to hide somewhere else every day now.

Well, that didn't help anything, they both thought.

'Emily, hurry up, we'll never get to school.'

They finally arrived back at school. Mr Smith hadn't locked the gates so they were able to sneak in.

'Come on, Emily, quickly, where did you find the dairy?' asked Tom.

'I think it was over there, no actually, it was definitely over there.'

'Okay, let's get digging then,' said Tom.

Half an hour later ... 'Wow, how deep is it buried?'

'Stop. I think I have just hit something.'

'Yes, I think I've found it,' said Emily as she saw some gold glistening like a million stars in the earth. She pulled it out carefully. 'It's so beautiful,' she gasped. ' We must take it to the police.'

Later on at the police station, Tom and Emily described the events of the day. The police explained that the Sceptre would be taken to a museum and that it was very famous and had been lost for hundreds of years.

Tom and Emily continued to try and find out what happened to Lord Norris and John. Lord Norris had been arrested and hanged for stealing Roman treasure in Winchester, soon after John had written his diary. They never found John and hoped that he may have escaped and found a kind family to care for him.

Emily was given a £60,000 reward and she gave half of it to St Bede School.

Emily Maynard is a pupil at St Bede.

The Girl in Malaya

by Robin Marriage

It was nearly closing time at the cosy little pub, which everyone called Auntie C's.

He'd had a long day in the little workshop behind the living room that he and his wife had converted into a profitable little antiques shop in the Stockbridge Road. And after two or three Ringwoods at the old Hyde Tavern it seemed like a long walk home. Putting off the moment, he picked up a paper someone had left behind.

An ordinary war picture, if there is such a thing, had caught his eye.

A soldier crouching in some armoured truck, looking down his gun-sight, scanning an almost empty desert street in a dusty brown desert village. His helmet and camou jacket were the brightest colours in the frame. In the centre a lone figure with an ancient, ramshackle a bicycle, stopped and looking back at the foreigners on patrol.

The caption said it showed the troops' fear of suicide attacks, a new danger, it said, requiring snap decisions of life and death and new levels of alert.

It was a dramatic, dangerous world, one he'd long ago left behind for another one in the shop, a world just ten minutes walk away in the rain, not what seemed like as many thousand miles away. He preferred his clocks to his wife's pictures and her shiny brown furniture, her objets and slightly threadbare Persian carpets. In the crowded little workshop behind the shop in Hyde Abbey Road there was hardly room for anything else, hardly room even for Geoff.

There were clocks on the shelves, clocks on the floor, clocks on his neat little workbench. There were more in boxes, bits of clocks, wheels and escapements, clock springs, clock cases, clock faces. In the corner was a slightly damaged chair, grown

151

dusty as it waited defiantly for a little care and repair. A tiny electric powered, desktop lathe would sometimes hum on the workbench, demanding total attention. It was a little like the machines which High Street cobblers use for cutting keys but this was clearly a precision machine. Brass finger-worn wheels, little knobbed levers, all spotlessly clean, the dull steel parts all fitting together like some metallic 3-D puzzle. In places the lathe was bright steel, blued with tempering at the cutting edge, with flats and facets everywhere, and the smell of milky-white cutting oil.

He loved the sound as it bit into a penny-sized brass blank, the motor gently whirring. As he brought the tool to the work, the humming dropped a tone or two and little piles of glinting gold built up below it, the new piece slowly growing cog teeth. Over the years he'd built up a reputation. Some of the clocks he repaired had probably not been touched for a hundred years. People came from miles away for specialist repair work on mechanisms worth thousands of pounds.

She'd always said it was the furniture that paid the bills, but it certainly didn't pay them all and many a customer came in with a clock to be fixed and left with a good feeling and perhaps a chaise long. Sometimes he'd buy a mechanism to restore and he usually managed to sell it without losing money. He'd be called in for valuations, sometimes to advise burglar-hunting detectives, uncertain auctioneers or suspicious loss adjusters.

It was a comfortable life, being paid to do what he'd do anyway. But that news picture from a desert village threatened to un-tune his hard-won harmony.

He couldn't recognise the soldier's firearm. It was slightly out of focus and its darkness and lack of detail was part of the photographer's image as the shutter clicked. He'd have liked to see a little more of it, to compare it to the weapons he'd worked on all those years ago as an armourer on national service.

It was the Army that taught him, scarcely more than a boy soldier, about machines and mechanisms, about cogs and cams, about catenaries and clearances. He quickly learnt to repair a jamming machine gun, calibrate a sniper rifle or make a recalcitrant mortar work again.

He put down the newspaper, nodded to fellow drinkers as they faced the February night and headed for home, as he considered again the two machines in his life, the ones which quietly measured time and the ones which noisily ended it.

It had been his trade. He knew the parts which wore out and how to make new ones which would last at least until they got out of the Malayan jungle, a maze of insurgent ambushes and booby traps, of perpetual danger and always possible attack. He learnt about metal and what could be done with it. He learnt about steel and how to work it, about brass and what to use it for, about springs and pins, about the harmless looking bullets, designed and made with ruthless precision to tear into flesh. He learnt how they behave in flight at a thousand miles an hour and the damage they do.

In front of the heap of logs burning in the old Tavern fireplace, he mused about his time in the Army, a lifetime away, about his friends and fears. He'd been with a jungle unit, tracking down Chinese-backed insurgents, hot, dirty, lonely and very, very frightening. He felt again a racing heart and the shivers down the back. He rarely talked of that life, not to his wife, not to their son, not to friends, not that he had many. Over the years, he thought about it less himself.

He could never be sure that anyone would believe his old-soldier accounts, even if they were interested. Perhaps they'd think he was boasting, or under-selling his stories for dramatic effect. Not that he cared much. They were history, not entertainment, his history. And, truth be told, the funny ones had become an affront to the people, some nameless, some friends, who'd figured in the not-so-funny ones.

But it wasn't just that. Over time he'd even begun to doubt their truth himself. His feelings had become so unreal that descriptions would have been second-hand, shop soiled. There was a loyalty, too, to those who were there. . . and to the girl.

He was wary of betraying friends and comrades, exposing them to the unspoken judgements of people who could never know the realities, revealing things which no-one who'd not been there could ever understand and would therefore judge. He knew all that and he kept it all in his head.

Now, in the smoky warmth, the safety and comfort of the wood-filled, wood-smoke filled Hyde Tavern. He remembered that village again, all rows of rubber trees, clumps of big-leafed banana plants around the huts. Chickens, pecked aimlessly at the dust under coconut palms. Pigs wandered about. It was like any other but he'd never been there before and never wanted to see its lying, fractured idyll again.

They were coming back off patrol, he and his mates, still jumpy and still a few days away from the comfort and security of the base. Any movement in the bush might have been an enemy, anything slightly unusual an ambush or a booby-trap. Any sound was a signal, any footstep a killer's.

Friends now might have been enemies only an hour before. There could be explosives in any village hut, weapons in any sarong, hate suddenly in anyone's eyes.

The career sergeant in charge of the patrol had posted look-outs as the rest cooked a meal, prepared for a few hours of sleep within sight of what they took to be a 'friendly' village. There were jokes and hot tea as someone produced a pack of cards.

Then a call from the man they'd posted on lookout duty.

Something was happening, unusual bustle among the huts 200 yards away, men and women in little huddles, children suddenly more interested in what the adults were doing than in their own games.

A group was coming towards them, away from the huts, men and children mostly, no sign of weapons or hostile intent, but what did they want ? They must have known there was nothing the young soldiers could give them or tell them.

The lookout shouted what amounted to almost his entire vocabulary in Malay. His tone, hard and slightly agitated, conveyed more than the jumble of words but the group shouted inaudibly and indecipherably back, and kept on coming. The squaddies quickly, desperately, tried to figure out what was going on. Perhaps they were being enticed out of cover to be ambushed in the open, perhaps the villagers were decoys for an attack from the rear, maybe the sarongs hid rifles or grenades, as so often they did.

If the patrol opened fire, even with warning shots, they knew it would alert the jungle guerrillas for miles around. And anyway, maybe the villagers really were 'friendly' and simply trying to say so. But, ran the counter argument, a gook is a gook, better safe than sorry... and they trained their guns on the brown, grinning Malays.

The little group stopped, shouted a bit more and looked back, standing in the open, apparently puzzled, aware of the weaponry pointed at them.

Geoff was not a big man, then or now. He wasn't really built for jungle work, which was often hand-to-hand fighting, with pistol and bayonet. He was only there as the armourer, looking after the weapons, doubling as cook and trying to operate what passed as radio in those days. But the training had made him a good marksman, that and his calm, methodical, engineer's temperament. He was the patrol's best sharp-shooter.

The Malays started coming forward again, talking among themselves and shouting to the British. Some put they hands up as they walked. Others were carrying baskets... every one in the cross hairs of a Lee Enfield. The platoon sergeant was regular Army. his plan was to let them keep coming, hoping the situation would become clearer.

Less than 50 yards away, a little girl broke away from the group, half running towards the platoon. Brown and smiling, her hair gleaming with coconut oil, barefoot and wearing only a sarong, perhaps six years old, with a palm-leaf basket that seemed to contain a freshly-killed chicken, all feet and feathers.

The sergeant, grim-faced and waving, shouted again, in English, then in Malay, then Cantonese. She waved back and started running towards them. He decided the basket was more bomb than chicken, an IED in the jargon of that soldier in Afghan desert dust, or at any rate, it could be. And he couldn't take the risk as she got close to his men.

They'd used children before as un-knowing bombers. He'd heard of it, then seen it, been warned repeatedly by higher-ups and blokes in the mess back at Changhi. Geoff crouched behind two feet of hard steel, his cheek snug against a warm, wooden stock, his finger curled around the deadly little trigger, closed his eyes and waited. The order was quite brief… fire.

As Geoff's single shot rang out, the girl dropped in silence. The smile that should have welcomed babies into the world, a husband home from the fields, grandchildren, would survive forever only in the minds of soldiers. The little brown body, lithe and shiny, was suddenly a jumble of bloodied arms and legs. The life it contained slowly spreading red over the dust. Only that smile remained, etched forever in a dozen memories.

They all left her there. The villagers fled back to their huts, their gifts, baskets of rice and fruit, stranded, abandoned, damning evidence of their good intent. The patrol packed up in a hurry and moved off. No one felt like eating anyway and the place was clearly unsafe now, even if it hadn't been before.

Geoff never told anyone, almost forgot about it until that picture in the paper. It released him from decades of silent guilt and fury. He tried, trembling, to explain to the barmaid, but she was more interested in clearing the bar and the empty glasses.

He wanted to tell the world of his pain… and the girl's and her family's, his colleagues' too, to tell everyone that Iraq and Afghanistan wasn't the first time. He wanted to tell them there is something wrong with a war that forces men to make such decisions, generals and privates, then, now and always, a thousand years ago and a thousand years hence.

He walked slowly home in the drizzle.

Robin Marriage is a television journalist, living near Hyde, trying to write with mind pictures instead of screen pictures.

Monks Road, 1993

by Paul Williams

Twelve feet tall,
Glaring through the bedroom window at my wife and new born son.
Broken teeth, Catweasle hair, robed in ripped denim, clout in hand
Heart-leap, anxiety, angst, abhorrence
Pure panic propelled me through the door
"Just done your windows, Guv."
"Twenty quid? Daylight robbery!"

Paul Williams drinks in the Hyde Tavern and this piece was 'a squib for the Crime and Passion Evening'.

The Secret Island

by Paul A Clark

Two brothers called Paul and Andy lived in a town called Winchester, near a park called North Walls. Their house was in a terrace, which was great for the boys, who had lots of friends living nearby. It was quite large with three big bedrooms. The good bit was that they also had a garden with seven apple trees, which dropped the most gorgeous apples ever. Paul and Andy used to bring friends round to No. 22 Monks Road to gorge themselves on these delicious fruits. On this particular day the boys woke up to some fabulous sunshine beaming through the curtains of their room. It was Saturday and week one of the school summer holidays. 'Yippee!' Andy said to Paul, 'Let's go out to play over the Park and see if we can get across the river onto the Secret Island.'

After breakfast, they set off down the road and over the metal bridge which led to the Park. The boys always looked over the bridge handrails and checked the river underneath to see if there were any trout swimming up stream. Today there was one. Paul threw a stick in to make the trout move, but it didn't; this trout seemed to mock Paul's effort! Andy laughed.

Skipping onto the grass playing fields they reminded each other that Mum had told them to be back in by 12:45 and no later for lunch. They made their way across the Park to the north east corner where the Secret Island was located. The river crossing to get to the island was not a great distance, and although the current was slow and the water shallow, there was deep 'sinking mud'. How would they cross? Andy walked along the bank and came back with an old plank of wood and some branches had been snapped from a tree. 'Paul!' scowled Andy; 'I hope you didn't break those from a tree'. Paul loved trees and hated people damaging them. Luckily for Andy he had found them as they were. 'No, I did not,' he shouted in a hurt tone. Paul had also found some brushwood, another old plank of wood as well as a discarded strip of metal. They set about laying it across the narrow stretch of river on top of a thick layer of reeds and riverweed. They would get wet but if they moved quickly it would be ok. Once they were happy that they had a fragile bridge to cross, Paul volunteered to go first. He put one foot on the first plank and it started to sink below the water line. After a brief delay he placed his right foot on the second plank and metal, then jumped with all his energy onto the muddy bank on the far side and started to sink in the mud. As quick as he could, he leapt forward and dived onto the bank and gripped the long grass, which stopped him sinking any more. He pulled himself up and yelled, 'Yes' back to Andy, with his hands in the air. Andy was nervously laughing at his mud-soaked brother on the far bank. It was his turn next! Andy looked at the bridge and pulled it back into position, as it very nearly flowed downstream. Andy knew he was going to get wet and muddy. He decided to take a little bit more of a run up. Oh dear! As he placed his first foot on the plank of wood it moved and he went headfirst onto the second plank and face down in water. Scrambling to his feet, he leapt up onto the bank and grappled with the long grass. Paul helped drag him onto the top of the bank, laughing at the very wet Andy. Miraculously the bridge remained in place for the return journey. The boys brushed themselves down, turned around, and looked into the thick wood on the Island.

***

None of their friends had ventured onto the Island before. It had a mystery about it and some boys told a story of having seen an old man appearing amongst the trees. Nobody believed them, though. As they walked into the trees they both tripped forward as though through a barrier. In front of them flew a bird, the likes of which they had never seen before. It had no feet and only one wing. The animals in the trees were making different noises compared to what they were used to. It was much more of a screeching noise, which made the boys shiver. The spiders were also much bigger! The pathway was lined with large boulders as if put there to lead the way. They decided to stay on the path and it eventually came out of the trees. They came across a concrete jetty looking out across a much wider, deeper river than the previous river crossing. There was a concrete area the other side. The boys thought this perhaps must once have been a bridge. Out in the middle of the river, were the largest reeds the boys had ever seen. In the river they spotted rather weird looking fish with one eye and huge in size. Andy and Paul took off their shoes and sat on the jetty dipping their feet in the water, which was very clear but cold. After a few minutes a large piece of polystyrene floated towards them and Paul reached out with Andy holding on to him, and grabbed it, pulling it towards the jetty. They both agreed to try sailing on it. Paul found a long branch, which they would use as a pole to direct the raft. Slowly they got on one at a time and used the stick and their hands to paddle down stream. As they picked up speed, a large fish leapt out ahead of them and splashed the raft. Then another did the same, which carried on for several minutes. These were the largest fish the boys had seen in their lives. Andy said, 'Are you frightened, Paul?'. 'No! said Paul, 'but I think that when we tripped into the trees on the Secret Island we fell into a different world'. Andy looked really worried.

Off to the bank to their right, some two legged horses with one eye galloped along beside them. Each had a one eyed bird sat on its back. How did they stand up straight? It all seemed very peculiar. The horses followed them for a short while, then reared up and turned away and disappeared. There were fish following once again that began jumping over the raft many feet above their heads. Paul and Andy laid flat avoiding the fish.

Suddenly a boy with the biggest ears they had ever seen was running beside them with his dog. It barked with a cough-like sound and the boy shouted in a scream-like voice, 'Hello, who are you? Come over here.' Paul replied, 'Who are you?' The boy said, 'my name is Jez.' As he said this, a dolphin leapt over their raft, right over their heads, getting them soaking wet again. The dolphin was so unusual with a really big nose and a big friendly grin on its face. They steered the raft over to the bank and jumped off pulling it onto the bank also. This was so exciting, a real adventure.

***

Jez was a really nice boy with a large brown mop of hair; very large floppy ears and he wore a bright green set of clothes with nothing on his feet. His dog was called Pip, a lovely small animal who was always jumping around, very excitedly. Like all of the animals they had seen so far he had only one eye. Jez called out to the river and used the name Rolly. Suddenly Rolly, a dolphin-like creature leapt out of the river into the air and wagged his fin, then dived back into the river making an almighty splash. Rolly was Jez and Pip's best friend, as they spent many hours by the river playing together. Paul and Andy told Jez that they had come to their Secret Island and seemed to have tripped into a different world where everybody and the animals looked strange. Jez told them that this world was called STANTIA, but could not give any sort of date or time that they were living in, as he did not understand what time was. As with all worlds though, he did understand day and night. Suddenly, they heard large footsteps behind them but couldn't see who was making the noise. Jez shouted, 'Hide!' They all ducked under the cover of a fallen tree. Then they saw who it was, a prehistoric looking animal, larger than the boys home in Monks Road. – Massive! Long legs, big ears, huge wings and a long beaked head. Jez told them that these beasts ate people in one gulp. Luckily it flew off across a marsh area near the river and out of sight. 'Wow, that was lucky,' said Andy. Jez told the boys to strip to their shorts and jump on Rolly for a ride. What fun! They both jumped on from the bank at once, not minding the cold water on their legs. They were taken for the most incredible ride at real speed. They flew through the air and under the water, holding their breath for what seemed like ages. Rolly returned them to the bank and they put their clothes back on. What an adventure! They would have so much to tell their friends.

***

They all walked further along the river to where Jez lived. He told them he had a brother and five sisters who were all older than him. They lived in a massive tree trunk with three floors. When they arrived they were amazed by what they saw. It was the largest tree ever. It had windows like Paul and Andy's house but no glass. There were about twenty windows all together. As they approached, one of Jez's sisters flew out of the top floor window on a rope slide. She screamed all the way down. She looked very beautiful and happy. She shouted out, 'Where do you come from? How do you hear with those tiny ears?' Paul explained and she laughed saying, 'that place doesn't exist, you must be joking'. Still laughing she rode away on a weird looking animal that had been tied to a small tree. It was like a horse but only had two legs. Both the horse and Jez's sister soon disappeared, screaming as loud as they possibly could.

Once inside the tree, Jez showed the boys up to his bedroom on the second floor, having passed many many other rooms. It was like a cave inside with lots of pets in cages hanging from the ceiling. These were birds mainly, all different shapes, sizes and colours. There was a slow burning torch flame in one corner of every room. The boys were glad to see Jez's home but wanted to explore more now. He gave them a drink of water, that tasted quite fizzy but nice, then they ran out down the path towards the river once more. They looked back at the tree that seemed to smile at them whilst in a moment all the branches moved quickly then went still – a wave perhaps, thought Paul and Andy. 'I wonder whether we will ever be able to see this house again,' said Paul.

***

They all arrived by the river again and started to walk back towards the Secret Island. Suddenly they saw Rolly and he leapt out of the water to greet them causing a big splash. Then they heard a shot from a gun. Along the river they saw a group of hunters. The first shot missed, and then the hunters started to run along the bank. There were four of them, two with guns and two with huge nets. The second shot was again very close but went into the water next to Rolly. Andy, Paul, Jez and Pip ran alongside Rolly back down river, being chased by the hunters. The hunters started to get closer so Jez shouted to Pip, 'Go home!' He ran off quickly, running for his life; he knew the way.

Jez shouted, 'Dive in' to the boys, who looked horrified. There was no time to lose though, so they all leapt in and grabbed hold of Rolly's fin. At very quick speed he dived down to the riverbed and into a cave. The boys swam to the edge and sat looking at the beautiful ceiling of stalactites hanging down. This was the most mystical of places. The stalactites were gold in colour and shone like diamonds. At the back of the cave was a waterfall and rock pool. Jez said, 'Drink the water, it is sweet – lovely'. Paul had a sip and it was indeed lovely. Andy was thirsty so he had a good drink also. They explored the cave and all its creatures that lived there. There was a dark hole at the back that looked like it went into yet another world, but there was no chance that Paul and Andy were going in there; it was far too scary. Andy wanted a stalactite to take home so he snapped one off as As a wonderful gold and luminous memory of their adventure. After an hour Jez said, 'The hunters will have gone away now so let's go back to the river bank. It will soon be time for bed and my Mum will wonder where I am.' 'Oh no,' said Paul, 'it is way past lunch time in our world, we must also get going.'

***

Jez gave them a shell each from the cave and instructed them to breath from it whilst holding onto Rolly with their other hand, for the return journey to the river bank. Andy placed the gold stalactite inside his shorts and then they dived into the water and held on to Rolly's fin. Rolly dived out of the cave and into the river and came to the surface quickly. There was nobody by the river, the hunters had moved away. The sky was becoming dark now in this new strange world. They all scampered onto the riverbank. All at once they waved to Rolly who wagged his tail fin and dived away. The boys had no idea of time in this strange place, as their watches had stopped after they had dived to the cave. They sensed it was getting late, though. Jez agreed to guide them to where their raft was and then said goodbye. He was a great friend now after their adventure together. Out of his pockets he pulled two stones, one for each of them. As he gave them, they shone bright like stars and then suddenly shooting stars shot across the sky, like it meant goodbye – safe journey. Andy and Paul slipped them into their pockets and each gave Jez a hug. Jumping onto the raft they slipped onto the water and paddled up stream, waving as they went until Jez disappeared out of sight. There were all sorts of fish following them and jumping in and out of the water even over the raft! Jez had not wanted to say goodbye, but was hopeful that they would meet again one day.

They soon reached the Secret Island jetty. Paul pulled them alongside and they dragged the raft onto the jetty, perhaps for another day.

***

They started running home back along the Island path. When they reached the river crossing they took turns to hop, skip and jump to the park without getting too muddy. Once across, they realised back in their world the light was also fading fast and that they had totally missed lunch. They were in big trouble with Mum!

Digger their dog was barking like mad when he heard them coming down the side passage of No 22. Mum was not happy. Her face was bright red with anger. She said, 'I have been out looking for you several times; you are both grounded tomorrow.' As soon as they had dinner she told them they were to go straight to bed and Dad would be told when he came back from work. Paul and Andy looked at each other and thought, oh dear!

They went straight to bed after dinner and looked at their souvenirs. Paul looked at his stalactite and saw that it has turned to stone and was no longer coloured gold or luminous with a sparkle. Oh well, at least they had the stones. They held them in the air in their darkened room and at once a picture of Jez shone on the surface of the stone. He was waving to them. Pip was jumping up and down and Rolly leapt into the air in the river behind them. Then the sparkle faded and with it the image of their friends. Perhaps it would come back another day.

What had happened that day, how had they fallen into that mysterious world? Paul and Andy were certain that they would go back again one day.

Major Paul A Clark of the Royal Marines wrote this story whilst serving in Afghanistan. He based it on the many adventures he and his brother had in the North Walls park (now River Park), including one such river journey on a large piece of polystyrene, where a friend and he were subsequently chased upstream by river wardens! He lived in Monks Road between 1971 and 1978.

Mrs King Alfred

by Nicky Morris

Oh, I love the one about my Alfie burning the cakes. It splits my sides, it does. Alfie in the kitchen for starters - that's enough to get me going. I'm a man, he says. A kitchen isn't a place for men. And when he sees that withering look of mine, he says, AND I'm a King. KINGS certainly don't do kitchens.

But I tell you - it's not the burning of stuff in the kitchen that worries me - it's the fact that this silly story isn't even about MY kitchen or MY cakes - what I want to know is more about the woman who did manage to get him into her kitchen! And from all accounts, she was a nobody - a lowly swineherd's wife - so he says. How's the wife of a pigman snared my Alfie? Did she wiggle her snouty nose at him? Did she paw him with her trotters? Or was it her curly tail that hooked him? Mind you, he's always loved a bit of bacon.

I've still not got a straight answer from him. It was the Vikings, he said. He blames them for everything! I couldn't face being defeated by them yet again - I had to get away some-where to think. I took refuge in Athelney and there she was. A simple woman who gave me shelter and sustenance. She didn't pester me with questions like you're wont to do! There was no pressure.

No pressure, I said. Ha! Leaving you in charge of her cook-ing. What's that, if it's not pressure?

She was called away, he said. Five minutes, she said. Just don't let them burn.

Called away? What important business can a swineherd's wife have that takes precedence over the visit of a King?

She didn't know I was a King.

Now that's when I got suspicious - how could she not know he was a King? Wasn't the crown a bit of a give-away? Or wasn't he wearing his crown? And if he wasn't wearing it, why not? The only time he ever takes it off is when he goes to bed. And was that why she was doing a bit of cooking? My Alfie always gets peckish after a bit of rumpy pumpy.

So, she was cooking you a cake and...

It wasn't a cake, he stormed. I don't know why people always say it was a cake. She was baking bread, woman! It was a rack of loaves that burnt not a bloody cake. Get it right.

Okay, loaves, then. You love bread - why did you let the loaves burn?

I was deep in thought about those plundering, devil-Vikings and in particular that savage, Ragnar Hairybreeks. I'd just set fire to him in one of his long boats and I was enjoying the stench of his hair in flames when I saw the flames coming from the peasant's oven - and you know the rest.

I wish I did know the rest! All I know for sure is that from that day onwards, things picked up. My Alfie built a fort, rallied his troops and got his revenge on the Vikings. I did hear a rumour, though, that Ragnar Hairybreeks had a bit of an incident in the bread-burning department, too. So, something funny's going on here. One of them isn't telling the truth. I just hope it's my Alfie who's the innocent.

Nicky Morris lives in Monks Road and is one of the instigators of the Hyde900 'Bring-Your-Own- Literature' evenings held monthly in the Hyde Tavern.

The Ghost of Hyde

by Kevin Barrett

Many centuries ago on a cold winter's night, an old woman on a pilgrimage to the Shrine of St Swithun journeyed to Winchester along the old Basingstoke road.

As she neared Hyde Abbey snow began to fall. Her threadbare garments offered little protection against the cruel winter weather. An old shawl framed her careworn features, barely covering her unkempt grey tresses. And her swollen feet were bound in rags.

She leaned heavily on her pilgrim's staff. Her frail body weakened from the ravishes of cold and hunger, as she stumbled onwards through the storm.

Patches of yellow glowed warmly from cottage windows mocking the old woman lashed by the blizzard. She desperately sought refuge from the storm, and a bowl of gruel to assuage her hunger.

She came upon a tavern. The peal of merry laughter from within uplifted her. She uttered a prayer to St Swithun, then summoning her failing strength, she strained against the heavy oak door that opened into a well lit taproom warmed by a roaring fire. She reeled unsteadily, giddy from exhaustion and hunger. And her dishevelled rags coated with snow would have evoked pity from the hardest heart.

The old woman's weak voice broke the uneasy silence that had greeted her entrance: 'Please, Sir, may I warm my bones and buy a few pen'orth of gruel?' she said to the tavern keeper, a portly red-faced man, his girth swollen from the rich pickings gleaned from passing travellers and pilgrims. His ruddy, usually congenial features when welcoming the wealthy to his tavern, turned purple with rage: 'Be off with you. Do you think this is an almshouse, you old hag? If it's alms you want, knock at the door of the Abbey.'

A company of young noblemen who had feasted well on a haunch of venison, and were merry from wine, were spurred on by the tavern keeper's outburst. They mocked the old woman, tossing her the bones that remained on their platters. 'Here, old woman. Here are the bones for you to gnaw on,' said one of the youths, gleefully.

'May St Swithun have mercy on you for your dark deeds this night,' cried the old woman.

'We have no time here for gypsy curses. Be off with you,' roared the tavern keeper as he cast her out into the cruel night.

The next morning three corpses were found in Hyde. A monk abroad early, espied a pile of frozen rags near the door of Hyde Abbey. On closer examination, he discovered the corpse of an old woman who had died from cold and hunger. Gripped in her clenched right hand was a talisman to St Swithun.

In the tavern, two corpses were discovered. That of the tavern keeper was found by the hearthside. In spite of the warmth from the fire, his body was encrusted in ice. His features, barely identifiable as human, were disfigured like a grotesque gargoyle. Whilst in an upstairs room, the corpse of a young nobleman was discovered. Although of a robust constitution, and renowned for his athleticism, a physician said that his heart had failed, similar to that of a man who had suffered a great shock.

Over the years, guests who have stayed at the Hyde Tavern on St Swithun's Night have reported strange happenings. They have claimed that a phantom intruder who pulled away their bedclothes disturbed their sleep.

In more recent times, a man on hearing the tale scoffed, dismissing the story of the Hyde Ghost as nonsense. He later confided in friends, telling them that almost instantly, he felt the touch of an ice-cold hand upon his shoulder. Although it was St Swithun's Day that falls on 15th July, he said he had shivered as if it was mid-winter.

Kevin Barrett, from Stanmore, is part of the Hyde900 Bring-Your-Own-Literature group.

House

by David Del Monte

The day before Fred Hilton bought my house I was furious. That reaction wasn't right, I know. It was totally illogical. Yet as that house stood next to my parents', I knew it should have been mine.

I told my father: 'Dad, we should buy that house. It was last on the market two hundred years ago.' He laughed.

'Oh yeah?' he said. 'It hasn't got a bathroom. It hasn't got a kitchen.

It's been used as offices.'

'Dad,' I said, 'I know that. I've passed that house every day of my life. I know it's been used as offices.'

'What do you want that house for anyway? You've got our house. Our house is your house. Use it as your own. Come and go as you please.'

'Dad,' I said (I was very young), 'it's not the same.'

'Not the same as moving out? You want to move out? Is that it? You want me to tell your mother you're moving out?'

'No, Dad, I'm not moving out. But if I bought that house, I would be next to you. We could put a hole in the wall and make connecting gardens; I could still come over every day. It would be like I was still there.'

'If you bought that house? If you bought that house? Am I hearing right here? With what are you going to buy that house? You haven't got a bucket to piss in. As God's my witness, have you done a day's honest work in your life? Can you put your hand on your heart, put your fingers into your inside breast pocket, take out your wallet, and hand me the deposit for that house? No, you can't fish out more than ten pounds. How the hell are you going to put down a deposit for that house?'

'I wasn't going to, Dad. I thought you might.'

'I might? I might?' He shook his head. 'You're very much mistaken, son, if you think that I would buy that house. What good would it do? You lie around all day. You're a bum, aren't you? A bum.'

'If you say so.'

'If I thought it was a good buy, I would buy that house.'

'Dad, it is a good buy,' I said. 'We can make an extension and build a kitchen and bathroom, and then I'd move in...."

He cut me off . 'It's out of the question.'

So Fred Hilton bought my house, at a snip, I might add. And what did he do? 'He proceeded to build an extension and put in a kitchen and bathroom, just as anyone would do. Over the last twenty years, Fred Hilton has married and raised two children in that house. As for me, I've been very happy, on the whole. I stayed with my parents. Dad was right, of course. His house was perfectly big enough. I could come and go as I pleased.

As Fred Hilton's children started growing up they would scale the wall on our side and on one occasion little Sammy dislodged some tiles from our roof at the gable end, which sloped down very low, almost to the lawn. I have to admit I screamed at Sammy. Perhaps I overreacted when I grabbed him by the arm, swung him off the wall, and dropped him over on the other side.

'Never!' I said. 'Never climb on that wall again, do you hear?'

He went running back to Fred, and seconds later Fred appeared on a stepladder at the border wall, all ginger moustache and sandy hair.

'What's all this about Sammy?' he asked.

So I told him what had happened and Fred said, 'You used unnecessary force. You almost wrenched his arm from its socket.'

'You should control him better,' I said.

That was the start of our feud with Fred Hilton. It was a very civilised fight, very British. No one said or did anything. I would sit in our garden listening to the raucous cries of Sammy and Lillian as they played in Fred's garden. I would watch as Fred worked on his house, painting the windows. I have to admit he did a great job with the extension. He really had a nice house, did Fred.

When I met Susan, my father said, 'You should have bought that house, you know.'

'Which house, Dad?' I said.

'The one next door. Look at the price of property now. The trouble with my son is,' he said, looking at Susan, 'he started late. He's got a good job but not enough for a proper pension. As for a mortgage if he buys anything now, he'll be eighty by the time he pays it off , that is if he can find an affordable house. That house next door is big. Where can you find a house like that on the market now? You can, but at a price. Now the best you can aspire to is a tiny flat. Tiny. Tiny rooms.'

But Susan just smiled and said, 'We'll manage.'

Dad winked at me and later said, 'Marry her. You're on to a good

thing there. Her father will give you the money for a mortgage.'

'No Dad,' I said. 'We're going away.'

'Going away?'

'To Spain, Dad. We're going to open a bar in Grenada.'

'What about your mother?'

'I'll go and tell her.'

So that afternoon Susan and I climbed up the hill behind the cathedral to the cemetery. I placed three daffodils picked from our garden on mother's grave. Then we went to Dad's house, and I packed and we left that very evening.

I sent some postcards to Dad over the years. Finally I heard that Dad had gone into a nursing home. He had to sell his house and use the funds to pay for his care. I thought about buying the house when it came on the market, but it was just too expensive.

When I went home to bury Dad, I passed our house and knocked on the door just out of curiosity. Who should come to the door but Fred Hilton's son, Sammy, very slender and tall with dark hair.

'Ah, I see,' I said. 'Mr Hilton has bought this house.'

The boy turned his head to the side.

'Dad,' he shouted.

Fred Hilton came to the door. He was much older. What was left of his hair had gone grey, his moustache still retained traces of sandy colour at the tips.

'Yes?' he said.

'Congratulations,' I said.

'What are you talking about?'

'This house. Well done. You'll be buying up the whole street next.'

'I haven't bought this house,' he snapped.

'He won't buy it,' said Sammy. 'he says it needs too much work.'

'I'm a surveyor. Did you know that? I'm here to conduct works for
  the new owner.'

'Who is the new owner?'

'The city corporation. They say it is a museum piece. They want to keep everything as it is. How long did your family own this house?'

'Two hundred years.'

'Pity you sold up. Th ey're going to have a nice income from tourists.'

'It's OK. I live in Spain. I enjoy the weather.'

'As you like,' he said. 'I hope you'll excuse me. I must get on.'

He closed the door. I went to the city council Recreation and Amenities Department to obtain details, and the man behind the counter put on glasses, scoured some official ledger, took off the glasses, smoothed his shirt, looked up at me, and said,

'There's no museum planned for there. The proposal was voted down at last night's council meeting in favour of a drop-in centre for the young unemployed and drug abusers. Local residents are rather upset about it. From what I hear there was nothing in there but a load of 1920s crap, in any case. Is there anything else I can do for you?'

I shook my head and turned to leave. On second thought I dug in my pocket and faced him again.

'There is only one more thing,' I said. 'Perhaps you might have a
use for these.'

I handed him my keys.

'What are these for?' he asked, holding the keys away from his body as if they were infected.

'Those are the front-door keys to your new drop-in centre,' I said. 'I may drop in myself from time to time.'

He seemed unsure how to react.

'You'd be welcome, I'm sure,' he said. 'But I don't think I can accept these. You would have to sign something. It would be better if you just hung on to them.'

'Or threw them in the river?'

He half-smiled at me, not sure if I was joking.

'Why don't you keep them, sir, as a souvenir to bring back memories?"

I looked at him and said I would.

And I have.

David Del Monte based this story on true incidents when he lived in Hyde with his family.

1538

by Simon Roffey

DUSK

The great church stood, sentinel-like, on the edge of the ancient city dominating the townscape clustered around it. As the sun set, the church's great shadow spread out, like a protective shawl, across the nearby lanes and houses – its square tower, a reassuring beacon, silhouetted against the purple evening sky. Purple, the colour of mourning, the old monk noted as he hurried from dormitory to church for what, he knew, would be his final evening service.

It had rained earlier and the slight downpour had made the rough cobbles of the cloister walk sticky and one or twice the monk's determined stride towards the church felt impeded - as if the very stone themselves wanted him to stay rooted here; his home, and indeed his whole life, here encompassed by the stout stone walls of the monastery.

The monk entered the chill cavernous interior of the church and stopped briefly on the threshold. Here, more than anywhere, he could feel the ancient presence of the stones themselves - reverberating with centuries of most devout piety. On this occasion however, he felt little comfort. Since he had arrived here as a young boy, some fifty years ago, he had always loved the smell of this building; the fragrant muskiness of recent ritual mixed with the damp earthy odour of antiquity. Around him, the slim piers of arcades rose up all about him, like some primeval forest. As usual for this time, the church was dim – the few small candles in the side and pier altars cast long shadows across the rough flagstone floor. The wall's lurid paintings, whose colours would shine vibrantly in the daytime, were now couched in shadow- as if in hiding.

He walked slowly toward the ornate timber screen at the end of the nave. Through the complicated scroll work he could see the high altar with its single spluttering candle. As it has always been.

The flickering light picked out the elaborate golden brocade of the linen altar cloth. The monk pulled up the hem of his dark robe and bent down on the step to pray. As he did, he noted that the candle burned low. It too was nearly at an end.

'Ave Maria... gratia plena, D-Dominus tecum'. His prayers came haltingly, his apprehension palpable despite the presence of the high altar. 'Benedicta...t- tu i...n mulieribus...'

He stopped, choking on the words, his concentration astray as he felt a deep welling up in the pit of his stomach. Then, an internal rush as the spiritual barriers that had protected him for so long came down, and as a torrent, his fears washed over him. Here, in the presence of the cross, within the church that had stood for centuries, its ancient fabric testament to the power of his God. Here, where joyous, he had shared his voice with his brothers, numerous and uplifted in the celebration of beauty. Here, now alone. The old monk felt alone above all else. Above the knowledge that these sacred walls would be torn down, the altars stripped, the wall paintings defaced and the eyes of saintly images pecked out by heretic carrion.

For the last time the great church bell tolled above, a single, sorrowful note. It was the End of Days. For the first time in many, many years, he wept.

DAWN

The young man was pleased that work was already underway. As he rode through the old stone abbey gate into the busy, noisy courtyard he saw a team of workmen unloading their tools from the carts; hammers, mauls and chisels were set on the ground along with the large storage crates which would transport the more fragile goods to the Court of Augmentations. Looming beyond the courtyard, silhouetted in the inky dawn light, he saw the imposing abbey church; the carved portals and niches of its west front casting a defiant chill shadow over the hubbub of the workmen. He noted, with some pleasure that ladders had been erected against the church walls and already some men were clambering over the roof. Dark patches spotted the grey slate as both tiles and valuable lead were stripped from their timber frames.

He dismounted and tied his horse to the post and made his way across the bustling courtyard toward the church. The smoke from the various melting fires and crucibles was thick here and he almost gagged on the purple sulphurous vapours.

'The devil's incense', he shouted to one of the workers, crouched, stoking the meagre flames from one of the fire pits.

'Aye, my lord, but God's work is it not?'

'Yes, it is my friend. Worry not, for today we indeed do God's work.'

'And the King's, my lord Commissioner, is it his work also?'

The young man stopped and looked at the workman. There was no hint of sarcasm in his face, but a questioning, a need, perhaps, for reassurance.

'Aye, and the King's, and for the good of the realm. Worry not, what destruction we carry out here will help rebuild a new kingdom, free of the yoke of Rome. Free of papist superstition and vanity. Rest assured my friend that God does not reside in stone or mortar, in gold and silver or in the alien mutterings of priests, but in good works such as that that we carry out here.'

He crossed the small bridge over the abbey stream which divided the courtyard from the church and monastic precinct. As he made toward the dark cavernous arch of the church's west door, he reflected on the marvel of what was happening today, and elsewhere around the realm.

Reform.

It had finally come after years of striving, secret meetings and plots, and the blood of countless martyrs.

Suddenly the large oak door swung open in front of him. An old man emerged, cowled, with a leather bag drawn at his side. Head bowed the old monk shuffled past him and then stopped and turned to face him. Their eyes met - the old monk's hot and red-rimmed eyes questioning - the younger's, cool and defiant.

'Good fortune, old man. You have no doubt served this place well. You leave, I know through no fault of your own, but change has now come, as God wills it, so fare you well'.

'No, my child, may *you* fare well,' the old man retorted. 'You have done great wrong here this day and thus the fires of Purgatory must surely await you. Rest assured, *I* will pray for your soul.' And with that, the monk turned his back and slowly walked away.

'Fires of Purgatory? Ha, another papist construct, monk, for enthralling the souls of the gullible. Look to thyself and hope to see out your twilight years in peace, crone. Worry ye not about me.' The young man turned away and continued on into the church.

Inside the spacious church he was greeted again by the sound of industry. Before him the heavy, ancient stone flags of the nave were being removed revealing the patchwork of orange mortar that lay beneath them. Ahead he could see the great timber screen already half dismantled, and behind it the altar. Stripped and bare.

Cold.

Yes, today was a new beginning, the young man thought; a time to break the shackles that had held back the good people of England for so long. It was a time of opportunity, for both yeoman farmer, merchant and noble alike. The churches would be stripped to provide rich fuel for change.

Above him, a single dull, clang resounded throughout the church. He looked up to the tower vault to see a team of workers struggling to remove the great iron bell from its mount.

Resilience.

Yes, it would take time, he thought. But his time would surely come, and his delighted laughter spilled out and echoed across the vaults and alcoves of the ancient church.

AFTERNOON

The man looked at his watch: **15.38** 'Ok, Emily, we ought to move along a bit if we want to have a swim, as well as get back in time for tea.'

'Ok daddy,' the little girl skipped through the cavernous interior of the old gatehouse. Her purple dress stood out against the dark stone. She wrinkled her nose at the acrid damp vapours of urine, alcohol and antiquity.

'Urgh, it smells in here daddy. Why does it smell?'

The man turned back toward the old abbey gate as his daughter emerged from the darkness into the small courtyard framed on two sides by a small neat complex of brick and tile houses. Startled, a team of ducks, plashed in the narrow stream, as Emily and her father made their way toward the small bridge.

'Well, hundreds of years ago there used to be a big monastery here and that gatehouse is really all that survives of it. Unfortunately, some people, er... misuse it a bit.'

'What's a *molas tree?*'

'A *monastery*, Em, a *mon-as-tery*. It was a place that had a big church and a group of people, called *monks,* who would live, work and prayer here- all surrounded by a big wall.'

'Were they prisoners then, daddy?,' Emily asked as they crossed the bridge, wide –eyed looking all about her at the narrow street with its terraced housing, but seeing little sign of any high walls.

'No, Emily, the walls gave them some peace and quiet. They didn't really go out much- well as least the ordinary monks - but here they had kitchens, meeting rooms, gardens and libraries- all sorts of buildings and most built of stone. Other people's houses in that time were normally wooden.'

They walked hand-in-hand along the street. At the end they saw the small public ornamental garden which led to the leisure centre which loomed in the background.

'And here, along this street, once stood the church; many important people were buried here.'

'What happened to it, daddy?' she asked as they entered the small neat ornamental garden, their feet crunching on the raised gravelled surface.

'It was all torn down, Emily, on the orders of a king, along with almost all of the other monasteries in the country.' Some people, called archaeologists, dug some of the remains up a few years back and this garden marks where part of the church was found. Look, that line of flints around us shows where the walls were, and those bushes mark the stone columns that once supported the church roof.'

Emily skipped across the gravelled platform onto the line of smooth flints that framed the gravel platform. Around her the column markers, an arrangement of shrubs housed in cylindrical frames, stood by like dryadic skeletal sentinels.

'Why was it pulled down?' the little girl pondered looking about her in wonder.

'Well, it was a time called the Reformation. Many people were arguing about religion and there where many different views. Some people did great harm to one another.'

'That sounds silly,' said Emily.

'Well, some believed that monasteries were greedy and owned too much land and wealth, whilst others believed they were generally a good thing. Anyway, in the end the king wanted a new wife (he already had one) and the church wouldn't allow it, so he set himself up as head of the church in England and then pulled down their monasteries!'

'He doesn't sound very nice, was he spoilt like Lavinia?' Emily asked, in reference to a schoolmate.

Her father laughed 'Yes, I suppose he was a bit.'

'And the monasteries, did they have swimming pools?'

'er…, no Emily, they didn't,' her father replied smiling.

'Well then, I'm sort of glad it's not here anymore, otherwise where would our swimming pool be?'

And with that they strolled off, hand in hand, as their laughter echoed around the pillars and walls of the ornamental garden.

Somewhere a distant bell rang.

Simon Roffey, from Swan Lane, is a senior lecturer in archaeology at the University of Winchester. He has lived in the city for nearly 10 years.

Hyde Garden

by Shaun Aquilina

The Abbey walls were last to disappear.
In 1539, men swarmed through Hyde like locusts;
The latest stop in a plague ordered across England
By that bloated King of History Henry VIII.
They gorged themselves on every piece of stone,
Gnawed at slate and lead,
And fled, bellies brimming.

Time did for what was left.
Decades of wind and ice
Splintered the ruin from inside,
Worked their long decay
To topple the Abbey
Crashing to the ground.

The sun seared the rubble
Till it prickled
And crumbled to dust.
Dust digested by soil.
Erased.

And while the walls dropped,
People dropped like flies.
And every memory of the Abbey,
Locked in old skulls,
Died with them.

2009:

The Abbey is a garden now.
No altars, just neat, round bushes
Spaced orderly and symmetrically.
You can stand
Where a monk once stood
But the designer ground
Has buried his footprints for good.

I try to build the Abbey in my mind:
Towering walls like Jericho or Troy;
Windows netting shoals of sunbeams;
The scratching nibs of monks at work,
Or chanting at vespers,
Slow rise and fall of notes
Shaking the air;
Sweet perfume of incense;
And sweeter, the herb garden;
Hospital, school, soup kitchen, sanctuary.

But the rush!
Clicking stilettos,
An ipod's base line,
Half conversations on mobile phones,
Break my Abbey.
The monks are frightened away,
Windows are shattered,
All is gone, gone.
The walls disintegrate,
Last to disappear, again.

Shaun Aquilina is Hampshire Poet of the Year 2010. He comes to the Hyde900 'Bring-Your-Own-Literature' evenings.